Homicide

Causative Factors and Roots

Richard M. Yarvis, M.D., M.P.H.

Lexington Books
D.C. Heath and Company/Lexington, Massachusetts/Toronto

Library of Congress Cataloging-in-Publication Data

Yarvis, Richard M.
Homicide : causative factors and roots / Richard M. Yarvis.
p. cm.
Includes index.
ISBN 0-669-24871-1
1. Murder—Psychological aspects. 2. Murderers—Mental health.
I. Title.
HV6515.Y37 1991
616.89—dc20 90-26047
CIP

Published simultaneously in Canada
Printed in the United States of America
Casebound International Standard Book Number: 0-669-24871-1
Library of Congress Catalog Card Number: 90-26047

The paper used in this publication meets the minimum requirements of American National Standard for Information Sciences—Permanence of Paper for Printed Library Materials, ANSI Z39.48-1984. ∞™

Year and number of this printing:

91 92 93 94 10 9 8 7 6 5 4 3 2 1

To Phyllis,
my most discerning critic,
my most vocal advocate,
my most valued associate,
my best friend.

Contents

Tables

Acknowledgments

I wish to thank the following people whose help made this work possible and significantly more manageable. Attorneys and judges throughout northern California were generous enough to refer the study cases to me. Without these referrals, the project would have been impossible. The attorneys painstakingly procured endless records and discussed the enumerable details of complex cases. These professionals are too numerous to name, but they know who they are, and I have expressed my gratitude to them individually.

Dr. Daniel Edwards gave hours of his time for discussions of concepts, theories, and methodological issues. He was of inestimable help.

Dr. Kay Blacker, chair of the Department of Psychiatry, University of California Medical School at Davis, was supportive of this research effort throughout its many twists and turns.

Professor Robert Burt of Yale Law School provided a perceptive critique of this work at a critical juncture in its genesis. The final product is better for his efforts.

Phyllis Yarvis, to whom I have dedicated this book, has been the mainstay of my life for more than thirty years. She has provided a benign environment in which the work could proceed, has typed endless drafts of this book, and has made suggestions about form and organization that affect virtually every chapter.

Introduction

When the murder of five children and the wounding of thirty others in a California school yard occurred, the community was outraged and demanded an explanation. While such a reaction is understandable, it is important to remember that homicides occur every hour of every day, most of them unnoticed by all but the grieving families and frustrated law enforcement officials. Can we prevent such events from occurring? In some instances we can, but only if we come to a better understanding of the dynamics of homicidal behavior. Hence, homicidal acts become propitious subjects for psychiatric inquiry.

Clearly, any complete explanation of homicide requires consideration of many potentially relevant etiological dimensions—social, environmental, economic, cultural, physiological, and psychiatric among them. A psychiatric focus is central, however, because homicide is the behavioral end product of mental processes. Other etiological factors do influence and impair or enhance mental functioning, but such effects are mediated through the psychiatric dimension.

This book reports on a study of one hundred murderers and considers four key questions:

1. What causal factors prompt persons to kill?
2. From a causal perspective, are persons who kill homogeneous or heterogeneous?
3. If heterogeneous, can we identify factors that can be used to aggregate such persons into meaningful clusters?
4. What can an enhanced causal understanding of homicide contribute to prediction, prevention, and case management?

Obviously, the present study is not the first to look at this subject, and it is disquieting that its predecessors have presented a range of findings that are discordant and contradictory. For example, rates of psychotic illness among murderers studied have ranged from less than 5 percent to more than 80 percent. The presence of substance abuse has been noted to be a relevant causal factor in as few as 3 percent and as many as 40 percent of homicides. The presence of sociopathic behavior has been noted in as few as 10 percent and as many as 30 percent of murderers. Psychiatric disorders in general have been discounted as meaningful causes in some studies and found to be almost universally important in others.[1–20]

The reasons for the observed discordance become more obvious when the psychiatric literature relating to homicide is examined in detail. Most studies have not examined a broad range of causal factors. Other studies base their conclusions on little more than anecdotal singlecase or multicase reports[21–28] and as such cannot accurately quantify causal patterns.

Even among the more structured studies, a number of methodological impediments may account for the lack of uniformity in findings. Many used unspecified diagnostic criteria, making results impossible to compare. In some studies, record reviews were substituted for direct clinical observations, and thus the authors had no basis for assessing the accuracy of the data reported. Also, both the nature and sources of study populations have differed significantly from study to study, and the kind of comparative data needed to assess sampling bias has rarely been provided.

The psychiatric studies of homicide to date have investigated a limited number of factors in noncomparable and not necessarily representative samples using ill-defined diagnostic criteria. Moreover, these studies have been conducted over a very long time frame during which diagnostic concepts have changed. Indeed, it would be surprising if the results garnered from such procedures were not contradictory and inconsistent.

The present study took these methodological issues into account. I used direct, in-depth psychiatric observations and adhered rigorously to well-defined and accepted diagnostic criteria. I examined a broad range of causal factors and consulted a

comprehensive array of informational sources. I also examined the issue of sampling bias. While this is not a perfect effort, it lends rigor to a subject that sorely deserves it.

I must beg your indulgence in one important respect. This book is not a legal treatise and does not rely on formal legal definitions. The word *homicide* is used throughout to include all forms of manslaughter and murder except those offenses determined to be accidental, justified, a consequence of self-defense, or the product of a vehicular accident. Also, the word *murderer* is used to refer to anyone who has committed a homicidal act as defined above. It is necessary to take this legal license because the word *homicider* does not exist in the English language and an alternative is needed.

1
An Explanatory Model of Murder

How is it possible to understand and explain homicidal behavior? Homicide is an intriguing subject. Consider, for example, the extremity of the act and the finality of its effects. Consider also the near universality of homicidal thoughts, which contrasts so vividly with the rarity of murderous deeds. All of us have been angry. Most of us at one time or another have been angry enough to think we could kill. Few of us, however, have ever committed a murderous act.

Any inquiry into homicidal behavior must address one fundamental question: How and under what circumstances do homicidal thoughts become murderous deeds? Given both the complexity of causality and the diversity of human responses to different causal factors, this question is far easier to pose than to answer. Complexity and diversity ensure that no single or simple answer to our fundamental question will suffice.

Issues of Cause and Response

Before we examine the issue of cause, let us illustrate the matter of diversity of response. Consider for a moment the following hypothetical example, which illustrates the range of possible responses to one provocative cause. Driver A is cruising along a highway. A's driving behavior is in no way discourteous or inappropriate. Without warning, driver B cuts in front of A's car. A's efforts prevent an accident, but only barely so. What is A's likely response?

A's emotional response can be predicted with virtual certainty: anger and disgust. But his behavioral response defies facile prediction with the limited information at hand. For the moment, the best we can do is examine the range of potential behavioral responses. Driver A may mutter and curse, cast aspersions about the lineage of B's ancestors, and then drive on to his destination. Alternatively, A may attempt some retaliatory activity, perhaps chasing after B to verbalize displeasure or even return the behavior in kind. A further escalation of response could involve an attempt on A's part to bring about a direct confrontation. A might force B to stop and then initiate a shouting match or fistfight. Finally, A could pursue B and then wound or kill him with a weapon taken from the glove compartment of A's car. Before the reader concludes that this last possibility reflects a pure flight of fantasy, consider the recent spate of violent episodes on southern California freeways.

What then determines the choice of response? To understand why a particular response is chosen, we must examine the complexities of cause. The following very brief vignettes introduce some of the causal factors that are relevant to our inquiry.

> J.J., a man with a pervasively violent and antisocial life-style, kills a customer who has not paid for the illicit drugs J.J. sold him. In this case, we can consider both J.J.'s antisocial orientation and the retaliatory motive as possible contributory causal elements.

> A.F., an unmarried male who espouses grandiose delusional beliefs and other symptoms of mental illness and who also exhibits an antisocial life-style, stabs a woman friend and leaves her body to decompose in his closet. In this case, both mental illness and an antisocial orientation may be contributing causal elements.

> B.H., a middle-aged, chronically depressed, alcohol-dependent man, demands restitution from another man who has allegedly cheated him out of thousands of dollars. When ridiculed, B.H. shoots the man. In this case, mental illness, substance abuse, damage to self-esteem, and the stress of significant losses may play causal roles.

E.S., a young unmarried man, is highly intoxicated when he encounters another man who has previously accosted E.S.'s mother. Taunted by the man, E.S. shoots him. Both intoxication and a revenge motive may play a causal role here.

J.M., a transient with no community ties, an extensive criminal history that includes violence, and a long-standing dependence on cocaine, robs and then slits the throat of a businesswoman. His rootless and alienated status, his criminal orientation, and the effects of cocaine intoxication may be contributory causal elements in this case.

C.S., a husband and father whose behavior has become increasingly bizarre, appears at his workplace one morning and kills his supervisor, claiming that the man is the devil and is about to harm C.S. and his family. The overwhelmingly debilitating effects of severe mental illness may play a major causal role in this case.

J.W., a chronically despondent woman, alleges that she has been repeatedly tormented both physically and sexually by a drug-dependent, philandering, and threatening husband and kills him. Depression, retaliatory rage, and the fear of imminent harm may play relevant roles in this case.

These vignettes introduce many causal elements and suggest that such elements operate together in complex interactions to produce homicidal behavior. We will meet each of these murderers again later. For now, let us return to our hypothetical example. Driver A's choice of response to driver B will depend on his state of sobriety, his mental health, his prevailing values, and the presence of concomitant stresses, as well as on the degree to which he is alienated and feels he has little to risk in the pursuit of some momentary satisfaction.

One essential task evolves naturally from the foregoing discussion: the compilation of a comprehensive list of relevant causal factors. Any such list will contain some factors to which

all experts can subscribe but also may contain or lack others about which there is disagreement. Also, any such list will be derived from its creator's knowledge about human behavior in general and violence in particular. I will offer my ideas about what such a list should include in the following paragraphs.

Causal factors are of two kinds, proximate and long-term. Proximate causes include all those that immediately influence current behavioral responses. Long-term causes are those that influence the crucial childhood growth and development experiences that shape individuals and influence all future adult functioning and behavior. Long-term causes predate proximate causes and contribute to their development.

Both types of causes are germane to our understanding of homicidal events, but only proximate causes can be directly and temporally linked to homicidal behavior. Long-term causes have a more indelible impact on behavior patterns, but they cannot easily be linked to specific current behavioral events. For this reason, any investigation of homicidal behavior must begin with an examination of proximate causes.

Proximate Causal Factors

A list of proximate causes determined to be relevant to the study of homicidal behavior is presented in table 1–1. Fourteen proximate causes have been organized into three subcategories—baseline mental functions, interference from psychiatric or substance abuse problems, and the effects of transient precipitating factors. The baseline mental functions listed in the first subcategory are always present and may be impaired or intact. The causal elements listed in the latter two subcategories are not always present, but when they are, they impair, tax, or even overwhelm the baseline functions.

Each of the fourteen proximate causal factors can be linked to measurable parameters of function. A brief description of each proximate cause is provided in the following paragraphs. A more detailed discussion of the parameters of function that can be used to measure the status of each factor is provided in appendix C.

Table 1–1
Proximate Causal Factors Relevant to the Study of Homicidal Behavior

1. Baseline mental functions
   a. The status of interpersonal relations
   b. The status of impulse control
   c. The status of reality testing
   d. The status of rational thinking
   e. The status of cognition
   f. The status of self-image
   g. The status of internalized values
   h. The status of integration/alienation and enfranchisement/disenfranchisement
2. Interference from psychiatric disabilities
   a. The presence of Axis I psychiatric disorders
   b. The presence of Axis II psychiatric disorders
   c. The presence of substance abuse problems
3. Effects caused by transient factors
   a. The presence of specific rationalizing or justifying motives
   b. The presence of intoxication
   c. The presence of significant stresses

The first subcategory of proximate causal factors, *baseline mental functions*, is critical to all human behavior. The status of such functions can range from wholly intact to severely impaired. Each function represents a personality mechanism that enables individuals to understand and interact with their environment and to cope with internal stimuli. Such baseline functions, operating in concert, facilitate problem solving. When such functions are impaired, the capacity of individuals to interact effectively with their environment is compromised. Brief descriptions of each function follow.

The interpersonal relations function enables individuals to relate to other persons in appropriate, consistent, empathic, and cooperative ways. Impairment of this function diminishes the ability of individuals to value other persons.

The impulse control function enables individuals to maintain control of their urges. When this function fails, outbursts of inappropriate, ill-conceived, dangerous, or self-destructive behavior results.

The reality testing function enables individuals to distinguish clearly and consistently between that which is imaginary and

that which is real. When failure of this function occurs, individuals are unable to perceive their environment accurately or to react to it appropriately.

The rational thinking function enables individuals to think logically, free from the intrusion of irrational, incoherent, or nonsensical thoughts. A failure of this function disrupts deliberations in thought that must take place before rational action can follow.

The cognitive function ensures that useful information will be perceived, retained, and later accessed for use in problem-solving efforts. Failure of this function depletes the data base on which normal decision making depends and impairs the decision-making process.

Self-image defines an individual's perception of self-worth. Impaired self-image can lead to outbursts of anger and self-defeating behavior.

Internalized values are the basic beliefs that govern an individual's behavior. When consonant with society's values, such beliefs lead to law-abiding behavior whether or not external constraints are present. When not consonant with society's values, such beliefs lead to antisocial behavior. Because individuals may not acknowledge "antisocial" beliefs, the nature of internalized values is best assessed by examining behavior patterns that are likely to be indicative of such beliefs.

Integration/alienation and enfranchisement/disenfranchisement are constructs that refer to an individual's sense of connectedness to and stake in the community. Integrated individuals feel linked to and a part of society. Alienated individuals feel cheated or ignored by society and are embittered. Enfranchised individuals feel that they have assets or resources that are worth protecting. Disenfranchised individuals feel devoid of assets or resources and hence feel that they have nothing to lose. As a consequence, they are more likely to indulge in antisocial behavior.

The status of the baseline mental functions influences all behavior and can contribute to the genesis of homicidal behavior. Obviously, not all baseline mental functions need to be impaired before a violent event can occur.

The second subcategory of proximate causal factors includes

psychiatric disorders and substance abuse problems. Not all individuals suffer from such disorders or problems. For readers who are not familiar with psychiatric diagnoses, these disorders fall into two major categories, Axis I and Axis II. Individuals may be afflicted by disorders in either category or both.

Axis I psychiatric disorders are characterized by symptoms that cause psychic discomfort in the form of anxiety, despondency, or guilt or by disorders characterized by inappropriate behavioral outbursts. I have clustered the Axis I disorders into four manageable categories: psychoneurotic disorders, psychotic disorders, behavior/organic disorders, and substance abuse disorders.

Axis II psychiatric disorders are also called personality disorders. While everyone exhibits characteristic patterns of personality traits, a person can be diagnosed as suffering from a personality disorder only if specific traits dominate all personality functioning in some clearly visible and highly maladaptive way. Eleven types of personality disorders are identifiable, each of which is characterized by a specific pattern of maladaptive traits. I have clustered the personality disorders into four groups based on similarities relating to the severity and content of their maladaptations. One disorder, antisocial personality disorder, is considered alone because of its prevalence among murderers. Borderline, paranoid, schizotypal, and schizoid personality disorders are clustered together because they are categorized by severely disruptive patterns of maladaptive behavior that are odd, eccentric, or erratic. Histrionic and narcissistic personality disorders are clustered together because they are characterized by intensely dramatic and/or self-absorbed behavior. Other disorders that I term low-impact disorders include avoidant, dependent, obsessive-compulsive, and passive-aggressive personality disorders. These disorders are clustered together because they are characterized by less disruptive patterns of behavior that are anxious, avoidant, or dependent.

Substance abuse problems may involve alcohol and/or one or more illicit substances. Substance abuse problems require a visibility above and beyond their inclusion among the Axis I psychiatric disorders because they may be accompanied by some other Axis I psychiatric diagnosis.

The preceding discussion has presented very complex material in a highly compressed and abbreviated way. If you are not familiar with these concepts, see appendix C. If appendix C does not provide enough detail, see the American Psychiatric Association's *Diagnostic and Statistical Manual of Mental Disorders*.[29] This manual provides the official diagnostic criteria for every psychiatric disorder and describes each disorder in great detail.

The third subcategory of proximate causal factors contains *transient factors*, which act as triggers or precipitants. Such factors are not always present, but when they are, they can turn potential homicidal situations into actual murders. Transient factors can work by promoting violent behavior directly or by taxing baseline mental functions to such a degree that they fail. The homicidal event occurs as a consequence of such failure.

The first transient factor listed in table 1–1 is the presence of some specific rationalizing or justifying motive. Such motives may be in some sense understandable, as illustrated in the case of E.S., who killed a man who bragged about accosting E.S.'s mother, or incomprehensible, as in the case of C.S., who killed a work supervisor he believed to be the devil. Rationalizing motives may involve widely diverse issues ranging from romance to vengeance. Murderers do not always offer motives and may kill for no discernible reason that they can articulate.

The second transient factor involves intoxication. Intoxication may reflect uncharacteristic behavior or may be the product of a chronic substance abuse problem. The importance of intoxication as a proximate factor will vary as a function of how much impairment it causes.

The third transient factor to be considered is stress. A wide range of stresses can impair baseline mental functions to such a degree that they fail. Stresses can be chronic or transient, but they must be active as contributing factors at the time of the homicidal event to merit consideration as proximate causes. Additional detail about all of the transient factors can be found in appendix C.

Long-Term Causal Factors

A list of long-term causal factors that I believe have a significant effect on the developing personality and particular relevance to homicidal behavior is presented in table 1–2. The long-term factors are organized into four subcategories. One can sense intuitively that such factors could contribute to the development of homicidal behavior, but it is a formidable leap to conclude that these factors cause this outcome directly. A brief description of each subcategory follows; a more detailed discussion can be found in appendix D.

The first subcategory, *negative parental and/or sibling role models*, takes into account postulates of social learning theory. Such concepts suggest that prolonged exposure to antisocial role models as might be exemplified in the behavior of parents or older siblings reinforces similar models of behavior in children. Pervasive criminality or substance abuse on the part of a parent, for example, could present a model that a child might then emulate.

The second subcategory, *instability in the childhood environment*, directs attention to two important attributes of such environments, constancy and predictability. Circumstances that destabilize an environment, as is the case when the integrity of the nuclear family has been disturbed, could adversely affect childhood development. The absence or death of one or both parents, for example, could cause such destabilization.

Table 1–2
Long-Term Causal Factors Relevant to the Study of Homicidal Behavior

1. Negative parental and/or sibling role models
   a. Father, mother, or sibling exhibited criminal behavior
   b. Father, mother, or sibling abused substances
2. Instability in the childhood environment
   a. Parent or parents absent
   b. Parent or parents died
   c. Parents divorced
   d. Father, mother, or sibling mentally ill
3. Lack of safety in the childhood environment
   a. Exposure to neglect
   b. Exposure to physical abuse
   c. Exposure to sexual abuse
4. Disruption of the childhood environment
   a. Prolonged medical hospitalization
   b. Psychiatric hospitalization
   c. Other institutional placement

The third subcategory, *a lack of safety in the childhood environment*, focuses on an important attribute of such an environment—security. Trauma engendered by neglect or abuse is very likely to have an adverse effect on normal development.

The fourth subcategory, *a disruption of the childhood environment*, focuses on circumstances that require the removal of a child from his or her home environment, with the attendant anxiety and confusion. This can occur, for example, if a child is hospitalized with a serious medical or psychiatric illness.

The impact of such long-term factors is far less predictable than that of the proximate factors. This is because the nature, intensity, and longevity of such factors vary greatly. Moreover, countervailing factors may be present to lessen the impact. Different children also cope with the impact of such factors in vastly different ways, some more successfully than others. Hence, the ultimate impact of childhood traumas on personality formation varies greatly and so by extension does their ultimate effect on adult behavior.

Despite such qualifications, it is valuable to examine the incidence of long-term causal factors among murderers. While proof of a direct cause-and-effect relationship must await longitudinal research efforts, findings garnered from this scrutiny can indicate what directions future research should take. Additionally, these findings may suggest, however tentatively, measures that might reduce or prevent the likelihood of violent behavior.

Other Frameworks for Examining Murderers and Homicidal Behavior

Two additional frameworks deserve mention in the investigation of homicidal behavior. The first focuses on selected demographic characteristics of murderers and homicidal behavior. A set of demographic factors is presented in table 1–3. These factors can be used to impose a familiar structure on a homicide, but this structure does not really add to a causal understanding of the phenomena.

The second framework examines the childhood behavior of murderers. An implicit hope in any examination of murderers is

Table 1–3
Demographic Factors Relevant to the Study of Homicidal Persons or Events

1. Characteristics relating to the homicidal person
   a. Sex of assailant
   b. Age of assailant
   c. Prior criminal history of assailant
2. Characteristics relating to the homicidal event
   a. Crime complexity—uncomplicated homicide, rape and homicide, or robbery and homicide
   b. Number of victims
   c. Nature of victim-assailant relationship

that it will uncover predictors of future violent behavior. Unfortunately, the only route to the discovery of predictors entails a cohort study design, which is both expensive and time-consuming. A large cohort of individuals would have to be followed from birth and their childhood experiences and behavior recorded. In this way, linkages between patterns of childhood behavior and later behavior, violent and otherwise, could be established. Given the expense and time requirements of such studies, they are rarely done.

More feasible but less methodologically sound are retrospective studies that seek to establish similar linkages by looking back at the childhood behavior of adults. Retrospective studies have two basic flaws. First, it may be difficult or impossible to recapture childhood behavior patterns accurately and completely. Second and more importantly, such studies can demonstrate the frequency with which a particular childhood behavior pattern occurred in persons who exhibit a later pattern of interest (that is, violent behavior), but they often cannot provide information about persons with the same childhood patterns who did not go on to develop the behavior of interest. Hence, retrospective studies usually examine only half of the vital equation. The use of control groups can mitigate these difficulties to some degree, but problems still arise with respect to matching samples. Despite these methodological concerns, it is worth examining retrospective data as long as these limitations are kept in mind. At the very least, such data can suggest relevant directions for future prospective research.

Five subcategories of childhood behavior relevant to the study of violence are presented in table 1–4. Each includes areas of childhood dysfunction that deserve consideration in the search for potential predictors of later violence. A wide range of dysfunctions that could indicate the possibility of trouble in later life is examined. Brief descriptions of each subcategory are provided here.

The first subcategory, *symptomatic psychiatric illness*, focuses on common symptoms that signal abnormal levels of childhood distress. These include psychologically induced speech impediments, phobias, and sleep difficulties. The symptoms chosen for inclusion are ones that are readily recognized by parents or other significant adults and thus can be readily and accurately recaptured retrospectively.

The second subcategory, *behavior difficulties*, focuses on destructive, temperamental, and dishonest behavior in childhood. Such behavior invariably disrupts the lives of the adults in a child's life and tends to be readily recalled retrospectively.

The third subcategory, *criminal behavior*, focuses on juvenile criminal activity. Such activities often come to the attention of

Table 1–4
Childhood Behavior Patterns Relevant to the Study of Homicidal Behavior

1. Symptomatic psychiatric illness during childhood
   a. Anxiety-related disturbances
   b. Disturbances related to basic bodily functions
2. Behavior difficulties during childhood
   a. Dishonest behavior
   b. Destructive behavior
3. Juvenile criminal behavior
   a. Violent offenses
   b. Property-related offenses
   c. Substance abuse offenses
4. School difficulties
   a. Academic problems
   b. Truancy problems
5. Difficulties with interpersonal relations
   a. Relationship problems with peers
   b. Relationship problems at school
   c. Relationship problems in the home

juvenile authorities and are recorded. Although these records sometimes are sealed by the courts, they can be obtained for review by defense attorneys.

The fourth subcategory, *school difficulties*, focuses on academic or truancy problems. Such problems are always documented in school records and are obtainable retrospectively.

The fifth subcategory, *problems with interpersonal relations*, focuses on childhood difficulties in establishing and maintaining relationships with teachers, peers, parents, and siblings. This subcategory is the most difficult to document retrospectively because relevant informants may not be available or may not have accurate recollections.

The specific measures used to establish each dysfunction are discussed in greater detail in appendix E.

A Strategy for the Study of Murderers

Chaos would result if all of the previously described frameworks were applied to a study population of murderers simultaneously and with equal weight. Thus, a choice between frameworks, or at the very least a prioritization among them, is critical. Even if one framework is chosen as a primary basis for understanding homicidal behavior, the others can be used in supporting roles.

Among the several alternative frameworks described, causal factors stand out as being particularly useful for understanding homicidal behavior. This choice should not be difficult to understand, as the frameworks based on demographics and past behavior cannot address the basic question of why a homicidal event has occurred. Only an inquiry into causality can do that.

The next choice, that between proximate and long-term causality, also is easy to make. Only proximate causal factors can be linked directly to homicidal behavior. Only they are demonstrably present at the time of a homicidal event.

The chapters that follow discuss the results of a research effort to understand the behavior of one hundred murderers based on the proximate causal factors framework. Long-term causal patterns, demographic patterns, and childhood behavior patterns were used in a supportive role to understand the study population.

Seven clusters of murderers were derived by an analysis of proximate causal factors using a statistical technique called cluster analysis. This technique enables an investigator to group or cluster cases on the basis of various attributes. Before a discussion regarding the clusters can proceed, an overview of the methodology used in the study is in order.

2 Methodological Considerations

Many of you may prefer not to delve into a study's methodological details and are interested primarily in its findings and conclusions. This chapter provides a brief overview of the methods that will allow you to evaluate the validity of the study's findings. Those of you who are more technically minded may demand a full methodological accounting. If so, you may consult appendixes A through E after reading this chapter.

The findings and conclusions in chapters 3 through 9 are based on detailed clinical evaluations of one hundred persons who committed one or more homicidal acts. These evaluations were carried out prior to each murderer's conviction, but all except two study subjects were ultimately convicted; the two who were not were judged to be permanently incompetent to stand trial. In every case, the evidence arrayed against the defendant was unassailable. Additionally, in seventy of the one hundred cases, the murderer acknowledged responsibility for the crime to me prior to his or her conviction.

The cases were referred to me for assessment by defense attorneys, prosecutors, or judges between 1980 and 1988. The assessments were not undertaken solely for research purposes but also to enlighten courts and attorneys about the psychiatric status of defendants. Given their sources, the one hundred cases do not reflect a research design in which random sampling procedures could be used. Such a design would have ensured the representativeness of the sample relative to the larger universe of murderers from which the sample was drawn. Only conclusions based on a representative sample afford a safe basis on which to generalize about a subject.

When random sample selection is not or cannot be used,

conclusions can have general utility if the sample was examined and found to be free of biases. In this study, the subjects were compared with all murderers convicted in California during two years, one early and one late in the study period. The specifics of these comparisons can be found in appendix A. The comparisons were by necessity limited in scope, but they were based on all available comparative measures. On the basis of these comparisons, a close match can be demonstrated between the study sample and the larger universe of murderers from which it was drawn. As such, generalizations can be drawn from the study findings.

I collected demographic, historical, and clinical information about each study subject in clinical interviews and from other data sources. An effort was made to ensure the reliability of all data collected (see appendix A). A data collection protocol was designed so that data could be uniformly recorded for each study subject. This protocol is reproduced in appendix B. Data elements from this protocol were subsequently used to assess the status of proximate and long-term causes and to study the childhood behavior patterns and demographic characteristics of murderers as described in chapter 1. In all, 297 data elements were abstracted, recorded, and analyzed for each study subject.

A host of methodological parameters are discussed in appendix A, but two specific issues that should be of interest to all readers—the maintenance of clinical objectivity and the procurement of complete, accurate, and reliable information—will be discussed here. While it is imperative that evaluators maintain both objectivity and neutrality in their evaluative efforts, the subject of homicidal behavior promotes anything but neutrality. Highly charged views come from every quarter concerning issues that range from the insanity defense to capital punishment. As is the case with all highly charged subjects, objectivity is at risk. The threats to objectivity stem from several sources. The first threat emanates from the very nature of the playing field. Murderers are referred for evaluation exclusively through the criminal justice system, a structure whose basic operating mode is adversarial. In such a setting, the evaluator risks being co-opted by one side or the other. The evaluator must be aware that this is the case and must protect clinical neutrality accordingly.

Clinicians themselves bring personal beliefs that can jeopardize objectively to the evaluation process. For example, a belief that capital punishment is inhumane could lead to an evaluation that reaches for psychiatric findings that would predispose a judge or jury to show mercy. Alternatively, a clinician who feels that all defendants should be accountable whatever their psychiatric status might discount relevant findings. Such reaching and discounting efforts, whatever their direction and however consciously or unconsciously they are pursued, produce a similar result—the loss of scientific objectivity. Even when a clinician does not impose personal beliefs on the work product, an evaluation may be influenced by a fear that he or she might not be retained in future cases if findings are not helpful. A clinician who needs the work or has a personal ax to grind should not do forensic evaluations.

Yet another circumstance in which objectivity may be breached concerns the relationship that may develop between an evaluator and a defendant when contact between the two has extended over many months. Defendants often try to be liked, not only to influence the outcome of an evaluation but also because they are genuinely seeking approval and sometimes forgiveness and because they usually feel isolated and alone. Objectivity can be hard to maintain when the evaluator is striving to establish rapport and the defendant is striving for acceptance. Interviews with the wives, siblings, and parents of defendants only exacerbate this phenomenon, given the distress that such parties visibly suffer. Moreover, no countervailing force is present to provide a balance, as clinicians rarely have contact with the loved ones of homicide victims. A clinician who cannot maintain an appropriate degree of detachment should step aside.

The opposite of defendant likability—attempts at intimidation—also can compromise objectivity. Though not a common occurrence, defendants sometimes threaten clinicians. Such threats need not always be taken seriously, but clinicians recognize that defendants may have associates who are not incarcerated and would be in a position to do the clinicians harm. Lest this seem farfetched, an ongoing case currently being adjudicated in northern California is worthy of mention. Allegedly, several accommodating associates of a defendant committed two copycat murders at his request to raise doubts about the defendant's guilt in an earlier case. These alleged copycat murders did not involve revenge directed at a clinician, but such a motive might be present in other cases. Attempts at intimidation or the perception of such can interfere with objectivity. A clinician who feels intimidated should ask to be replaced.

The second issue that confronts every evaluator is the need for complete, accurate, and reliable information. The experienced clinician recognizes that most sources of information in homicide cases have some vested interest in the outcome and must be considered with care. Defendants hope to minimize the consequences of their acts. Sociopathic defendants in particular can be quite persuasive in their attempts to fool gullible clinicians. Also, family members are swayed by issues of loyalty, love, and sometimes hate. Witnesses to a crime may have had a relationship with the victim or the assailant, and the trauma inherent in the event may have distorted their perceptions. Police investigators also may be swayed by their conclusions about the guilt of a defendant or their desire to achieve closure in a case. Although attorneys rarely provide misinformation, they do occasionally withhold information that is detrimental to their aims but would be useful in assessing homicidal behavior. Although employers, teachers, neighbors, and other informants may be more impartial, even they can be guilty of distortion. Even historical records concerning behavior must be used with care. Such records can be inaccurate and sometimes contain opinions that have been mislabeled as facts. No information can be accepted at face value and without corroboration.

Are these pitfalls avoidable? The answer is yes, provided sufficient care is taken. Clinicians must maintain a clear awareness of their personal beliefs as they go about their work. Beliefs that have been ignored or denied are more likely to contaminate evaluations than are those given full recognition. Clinicians who share a vested interest in the outcome of a case should not conduct forensic evaluations. Also, clinicians must maintain a suitable degree of professional detachment from their subjects. Rapport with defendants is necessary and desirable, but such rapport should not escalate into an emotional entanglement. Clinicians should withdraw from cases in which empathy or fear may contaminate the work product. Clinicians should not become economically dependent on criminal justice system referrals. Finally, clinicians should insist on complete disclosure. They must not settle for abridged records or transcripts and must maintain a benevolent skepticism with regard to all information provided in the assessment process. Facts and opinions must be labeled as such. The former should be corroborated by multiple sources before being accepted; the latter should be excluded from consideration.

There is no way to prove my objectivity with respect to the assessment of the one hundred murderers who were the subjects of this study. However, all of the above cautions were applied to the evaluations, and all possible vigilance was exercised to avoid the pitfalls described.

The technique of cluster analysis was applied to data collected from the study subjects using the fourteen proximate causal factors as attributes and the one hundred homicide defendants as cases. For purposes of analysis, each baseline personality function was assessed to determine whether it was intact or impaired, and each transient precipitating factor was assessed for its presence or absence. Also, the nature of psychiatric and substance abuse problems, if any, was noted in each case. Based on all of these considerations, a cluster analysis procedure sorted the one hundred cases into seven discrete clusters such that the similarities of group members in any cluster were maximized. A more detailed description of cluster analysis can be found in appendix A. These clusters, A through F, are the subject of this book. They are discussed in detail in chapters 3 through 9 and can be broadly categorized as follows:

A. A prototypical cluster of murderers with multiple personality dysfunctions and antisocial values who are disenfranchised and alienated

B. A cluster of murderers who share the prototypical pattern and are also psychotic

C. A cluster of murderers who share the prototypical pattern and also suffer from psychoneuroses, exhibit impairment of self-esteem, and have been overwhelmed by stress

D. A cluster of intoxicated, substance-abusing murderers with multiple personality dysfunctions
E. A cluster of intoxicated, substance-abusing murderers with patterns of pervasive antisocial attitudes and behavior
F. A cluster of murderers who are not antisocial but are psychotic
G. A cluster of murderers who are not antisocial but are psychiatrically impaired although not psychotic and have been overwhelmed by stress

Taken together, these clusters afford a comprehensive set of profiles that can be used to explain all homicidal behavior.

3
Personality Dysfunction, Alienation, and Homicide

This chapter examines the prototypical homicide cluster, cluster A. As the word *prototype* implies, cluster A is characterized by a core set of proximate causal factors that we will encounter repeatedly as we examine other homicide clusters. The prototypical murderer has problematic interpersonal relations, has poor control over impulses, and is likely to exhibit a long-standing sense of alienation and pervasive antisocial behavior. In addition, he or she usually meets the criteria for a diagnosis of some type of personality disorder. Operating together, this combination of factors represents a formidable prescription for violence. Clusters B, C, D, and E share many of the prototype's causal elements but are distinguishable from it by the absence of some core factors and by the presence of other noncore factors. In contrast, clusters F and G have relatively little in common with the prototype and can be termed atypical clusters.

The Proximate Causal Pattern

Cluster A comprises 20 percent of the study population. Using illustrative case examples, I will breathe life into the prototypical murderer. Later I will expand on each illustration.

> J.J., a thirty-year-old unmarried male and a dealer in illicit drugs, already had prior convictions for aggravated assault and rape when he killed one of his drug customers. J.J. initially denied responsibility for the crime

but ultimately acknowledged his guilt in the face of convincing physical evidence. He would not, however, discuss the details of the crime, nor would he acknowledge the precise nature of his relationship with the victim despite independent evidence suggesting that an unpaid drug debt was his likely motive.

J.J.'s relationships with people could be described as exploitive and, when necessary, predatory. When thwarted, he characteristically reacted with violent outbursts. This is exemplified by one instance in which J.J. stabbed a girlfriend who refused some demand, a second instance in which he raped his half-brother's wife after she resisted his sexual advances, and a third in which he sexually assaulted and later tried to kill a stranger to whom he was attracted. J.J.'s need to gratify the urge of the moment and to punish resistance was never constrained by any internal restraints.

No Axis I psychiatric disorder was diagnosed in J.J.'s case, but the criteria for an Axis II diagnosis of antisocial personality disorder were easily met. J.J. could be characterized as someone who manifested chronic and pervasive antisocial behavior, a lack of any responsible adult functioning, a history of unstable relationships, periodic aggressiveness, pervasive impulsivity, and repeated lying and conning behavior, all criteria for this diagnosis. He expressed undisguised disdain for society, which he viewed as having given him nothing and hence as being owed nothing.

L.T., a thirty-year-old divorced male, was working as a free-lance auto mechanic when he killed a man whom he described as both a friend and roommate. L.T. maintained that his victim was implicated in the death of another friend and, while acknowledging his responsibility for the murder, insisted that he had acted in self-defense, a contention not supported by evidence at the murder scene. L.T.'s efforts to hide the evidence of his crime and flee to another state did not enhance his credibility.

L.T. displayed many of the characteristics manifested by J.J., albeit in a less extreme manner. A self-described loner, L.T. was divorced by his wife after he abused her. Repeated outbursts of rage were found in L.T.'s history in circumstances when he was thwarted. Even when not violent, L.T.'s approach to people usually was intimidating.

Like J.J., L.T. did not meet the criteria for an Axis I psychiatric diagnosis but did meet the criteria for an Axis II diagnosis of antisocial personality disorder. Unlike J.J., L.T. denied feelings of alienation.

M.M., a thirty-six–year–old divorced male, was living with a girlfriend, her child, and another couple in a communal arrangement when he killed the other couple. M.M. worked at odd jobs and sold illicit drugs for monetary support. He had previously led a biker life-style, as did his victims, whom M.M. contended were about to kill him when he killed them. Aside from his victims' unsavory reputations, M.M. could provide no evidence to support this assertion. Moreover, his woman victim had been shot in the back, and after the murders, M.M. had attempted to hide all evidence of his crime by dismembering both bodies and scattering their parts around the community.

M.M.'s history included a succession of immature, hostile, and self-destructive relationships. The addicted and psychiatrically impaired girlfriend with whom he was living at the time of his crime was only the latest of these. M.M.'s history also revealed a pattern of explosive outbursts that he usually regretted and explained away by saying that he had been provoked.

M.M. reported no history of psychiatric symptoms, but he did acknowledge past drug abuse problems. Like J.J. and L.T., M.M. met the criteria for an Axis II diagnosis of antisocial personality disorder. Antisocial behavior had begun in late adolescence and continued after his military service in Vietnam. While M.M. acknowledged that he had been a thief, he did not openly espouse antisocial values. He related in a low-key and superficially friendly way, eschewing the overt hostility and intimidation that characterized the behavior of J.J. and L.T. M.M. admitted to having always felt like an outsider, passed over and ignored by society.

T.A., twenty-two years old and unmarried, killed an eleven-year-old girl. A drifter and part-time carnival worker, T.A. was visiting his hometown when he enticed his victim to a secluded area where he sexually assaulted her and then, hearing a passerby, stuffed plastic sheeting into her mouth to keep her from crying out. This caused death by asphyxiation. T.A. initially denied all responsibility for his crime but finally acknowledged his guilt. Still he maintained that neither the sexual crime nor the homicide had been planned but were the products of impulsive decisions of the moment.

T.A. avoided adult interactions and generally associated with children or immature adolescents. He did so in characteristically immature ways. For example, while awaiting trial, he talked about having become "engaged" to a thirteen-year-old girl with whom he was corresponding by mail. Although initially ingratiating towards others, T.A. quickly resorted to anger when frustrated. He had no prior history of criminal violence but had committed acts of petty theft. It was not unusual for him to leave jobs impulsively, without giving any thought to the consequences.

T.A. had no history of psychiatric symptoms but did meet the criteria for an Axis II diagnosis of antisocial personality disorder. T.A. epitomized the alienated, disenfranchised drifter detached from society. His antisocial and hostile attitudes typically were expressed more covertly than were those of J.J. and L.T. and generally were directed against much younger, and therefore more defenseless, victims.

J.M., an unmarried eighteen-year-old male, was living in his mother's home when he stabbed his mother's boy-

> friend. The victim had asked J.M. to leave the home for a few hours while he calmed down and gained control over his aggressive behavior. According to witnesses, J.M., without any verbal response to this request, proceeded to the kitchen, retrieved a knife, and stabbed his victim.
>
> According to those who knew him, all of J.M.'s interactions were primitive, predatory, and based on intimidation. His impulsivity was described vividly by one victim who recalled how J.M. had attacked her with a bottle, splitting open her scalp.
>
> J.M. demonstrated evidence of mild developmental disability, an Axis I psychiatric disorder. This disorder was, in all probability, a consequence of fetal alcohol syndrome, a result of his mother's heavy alcohol intake throughout her pregnancy. J.M. also met the criteria for the Axis II psychiatric diagnosis of borderline personality disorder on the basis of his impulsivity and unpredictability, the pattern of unstable relationships, intermittent outbursts of anger, sudden shifts in mood, and chronic feelings of emptiness and boredom. J.M.'s predatory behavior, which had resulted in several prior convictions for assault, demonstrated poor impulse control and a lack of socialization. His lack of any skills, resources, assets, or prospects left him feeling angry, alienated, and disenfranchised. Despite all of the evidence to the contrary, J.J. continued to insist that he had killed his victim to protect his mother from harm.

These case examples do not provide the only means by which the characteristics of this cluster can be demonstrated. Equally informative is a quantitative assessment of the proximate causal pattern of all twenty cases in the cluster. The necessary data are presented in table 3–1. The table lists the percentage of cluster members who manifested each proximate cause, as well as comparative data for the entire study population. The latter data provide an opportunity to identify differences between the prototype cluster and the study population as a whole.

The data in table 3–1 demonstrate that the case illustrations

Table 3–1
Percent of Cluster A Cases and Total Study Sample Cases in Which Specific Proximate Causal Factors Were Present

Proximate Cause Category	*Cluster A (n = 20)*	*Total Sample (n = 100)*
Baseline mental functions		
Impaired interpersonal relations	95.0	89.0
Impaired impulse control	85.0	79.0
Impaired reality testing	0.0	27.0
Impaired thinking	5.0	32.0
Impaired cognition	5.0	12.0
Impaired self-image	5.0	32.0
Antisocial values	75.0	65.0
Alienation/disenfranchisement	75.0	79.0
Presence of Axis I symptomatic psychiatric disorders		
Psychoses	0.0	28.0
Psychoneuroses	5.0	16.0
Substance abuse disorders	0.0	34.0
Behavior/organic/mental retardation	25.0	8.0
No Axis I disorder	70.0	14.0
Presence of Axis II personality disorders		
Antisocial personality	50.0	38.0
Borderline, paranoid, schizoid, or schizotypal personality	35.0	23.0
Histrionic or narcissistic personality	5.0	2.0
Low-impact disorders (avoidant, dependent, obsessive-compulsive, or passive-aggressive)	0.0	11.0
No Axis II disorder	10.0	26.0
Presence of substance abuse problems (with or without diagnosis of substance abuse disorder)		
Alcohol abuse only	5.0	19.0
Drug abuse only	5.0	14.0
Both alcohol and drug abuse	10.0	26.0
Presence of transient factors		
Rationalizing or justifying motives	70.0	65.0
Intoxication	5.0	48.0
Significant stress	40.0	50.0

accurately characterize the cluster. Impairment of interpersonal relations and impulse control is almost universally present. Seventy percent of all cases in the cluster manifested no Axis I psychiatric disorder, but Axis II personality disorders were present in all but 10 percent of the cases. Antisocial personality disorders were the most common. The presence of antisocial values and feelings of alienation also were common. While rationalizing motives often appeared in the guise of self-defense, 30 percent of these murderers persistently denied all responsibility for their crimes. Conflicts over money and homicides committed in conjunction with other felonies accounted for seven (35 percent) of the remaining cases.

Using both the case examples and the quantitative data, it is possible to delineate a common profile of proximate causes that link the twenty prototype cases together:

1. Almost all exhibited impairments of interpersonal relations and impulse control.
2. Many did not suffer from any Axis I psychiatric disorder.
3. Almost all met the criteria for the diagnosis of some kind of Axis II personality disorder, frequently an antisocial personality disorder.
4. In most cases, a failure of socialization and the presence of antisocial values was noted.
5. Most expressed a long-standing sense of alienation and/or disenfranchisement.
6. Many offered some rationalizing motive for their crime or persistently denied any responsibility for it.

The Demographic Pattern

Now that the prototype's proximate causal profile has been delineated, a demographic perspective can be used in a supportive role. The results of the demographic analysis of this cluster are presented in table 3–2.

An examination of the table reveals that most prototype murderers were male, many between the ages of eighteen and thirty-nine. A sizable majority killed only once and knew their victims. Prior criminal convictions were common. Almost two-thirds of these murderers committed uncomplicated homicides, but a surprising 35 percent committed complex crimes, either

Table 3–2
Percent of Cluster A Cases and Total Study Sample Cases in Which Specific Demographic Characteristics Were Present

Demographic Category	*Cluster A (n = 20)*	*Total Sample (n = 100)*
Assailant is male	90.0	88.0
Assailant is female	10.0	12.0
Assailant has prior criminal convictions	65.0	56.0
Assailant has no prior criminal convictions	35.0	44.0
Victim is known to assailant	70.0	67.0
Victim is not known to assailant	30.0	33.0
Assailant committed homicide only	65.0	79.0
Assailant committed homicide and rape	25.0	10.0
Assailant committed homicide and robbery	10.0	11.0
Assailant is younger than 18 years old	5.0	6.0
Assailant is 18 to 24 years old	25.0	27.0
Assailant is 25 to 39 years old	50.0	52.0
Assailant is 40 years or older	20.0	15.0
Assailant killed only one victim	70.0	77.0
Assailant killed more than one victim	30.0	23.0

homicide and rape or homicide and robbery. Except for this last observation, no significant differences between the prototype and the whole study population were observed.

The Long-Term Causal and Childhood Behavior Patterns

Two additional frameworks—long-term cause and childhood behavior—were suggested in chapter 1 as providing complementary perspectives to that of proximate cause. To examine these frameworks in the context of the illustrative case examples, we must know more about each case history.

> J.J. is described as having had an overprotective mother who set no behavioral limits and rationalized his adolescent criminality as "growing pains." No male role model was ever present in the home. J.J.'s mother suffered from chronic alcoholism, and when intoxicated, she was physi-

cally abusive toward her twelve children. Years of J.J.'s childhood were disrupted by placements in state hospitals and juvenile justice facilities. These dispositions were the result of constant fights and incorrigible behavior, including lying, stealing, and setting fires. Marked difficulties were observed at school, and ultimately J.J. dropped out of high school. By the end of adolescence, J.J. had an extensive criminal record.

L.T. was raised primarily by an alcoholic mother, as his parents had divorced when he was ten years of age. He suffered serious neglect when the mother was drinking and became the target of her physical abuse at such times as well. L.T. engaged in illicit drug use during adolescence, failed as a student, and dropped out of high school. He was described as a wild adolescent but was not institutionalized and had no juvenile criminal record.

Unlike J.J. and L.T., M.M. came from an intact family, but his father was an alcoholic. The father was frequently absent from the home for prolonged periods because of alcohol-related illnesses that required hospitalization. Physical abuse at the hands of the father was suspected but could not be corroborated. M.M. had no documented history of behavioral difficulties prior to adolescence. From that time on, however, M.M. abused drugs and alcohol, engaged in petty thefts, and was generally irresponsible. M.M. managed to complete high school but failed at a junior college. He served in Vietnam and upon his return joined a motorcycle gang and continued various antisocial pursuits.

T.A. was neglected by both parents, who fought with each other continuously and ultimately divorced. He was severely abused by his mother, who beat him frequently with a belt buckle and pulled clumps of hair from his scalp. T.A.'s incorrigible behavior led to long placements in group homes. His only consistent role model was a slightly younger but dominant brother who engaged in

> criminal behavior and substance abuse. T.A. tortured and killed small animals as a child, was hostile in most of his interactions with peers, exhibited behavior problems in school, and engaged in repetitive runaway behavior, stealing, and vandalism. He did not complete the eleventh grade.

> J.M. grew up without a father and was raised by an alcoholic mother. An older brother had a criminal history, and other siblings had substance abuse problems. J.M.'s mother frequently abused him when intoxicated. He was incarcerated in juvenile facilities several times during adolescence. J.M. also had a documented history of cruelty to animals. He repetitively destroyed other children's toys without provocation. His adolescent criminal history included convictions for burglary, assault, and sexual battery. He managed to complete the ninth grade by attending special education classes.

The case illustrations reveal that parental alcoholism was prominent for these murderers and that few positive role models of any kind were available during childhood. Positive male role models were especially scarce. Physical abuse occurred frequently.

If one examines the pattern of long-term causal factors in all the prototypical cases (table 3–3), pervasive evidence of childhood trauma is evident. The proportion of cases exposed to trauma exceeds 50 percent for each of the four subcategories. Childhood environments were noted to be unsafe and unstable in almost 75 percent of the cases.

When individual long-term causal measures are examined, the incidence rates of seven measures are especially striking. Substance abuse among mothers, criminal behavior and substance abuse among siblings, the prolonged absence of at least one parent, exposure to neglect or physical abuse, and disruption as a consequence of institutional placement all occurred in at least 25 percent of the prototypical cases. Several things suggest that the very low rate of exposure to sexual abuse may be misleading. Recollections of sexual abuse often are repressed, and even

Table 3–3
Percent of Cluster A Cases and Total Study Sample Cases in Which Specific Long-Term Causal Factors Were Present

Long-Term Cause Category	*Cluster A*[a] *(n = 20)*	*Total Sample*[b] *(n = 100)*
Any negative role models	55.6	51.0
Father had criminal history	17.6	8.9
Father had substance abuse problems	11.8	31.1
Mother had criminal history	5.3	3.1
Mother had substance abuse problems	26.3	16.7
Sibling had criminal history	31.6	27.1
Sibling had substance abuse problems	36.8	32.3
Any instability in childhood environment	72.2	61.0
One parent absent	68.4	53.1
Both parents absent	10.5	18.4
One or both parents died	5.3	12.2
One or more siblings died	0.0	2.0
Father was mentally ill	5.6	6.5
Mother was mentally ill	10.5	9.2
Sibling was mentally ill	5.3	9.2
Parents were divorced	63.2	45.4
Any lack of safety in childhood environment	73.7	59.0
Exposure to physical abuse	36.8	30.6
Exposure to sexual abuse	5.3	8.2
Exposure to pervasive neglect	63.2	55.1
Any disruption in childhood environment	52.6	38.0
Placement in institutional setting	47.4	33.7
Hospitalization in medical setting	10.5	7.1
Hospitalization in psychiatric setting	10.5	7.1

[a]Some missing data for three cases.
[b]Some missing data for eleven cases.

when abuse is remembered, it may not be revealed, especially by males. Since such abuse frequently goes unreported during childhood, it is not recoverable from records. It is probable, therefore, that childhood sexual abuse was more prevalent in this population than the study findings indicate.

The case illustrations reveal that antisocial behavior, so prominent in the adult lives of prototypical murderers, began during childhood or adolescence. In addition, school performance and peer relations usually were poor.

When one examines the childhood behavior quantitatively, the profile already revealed by the case examples is substantiated. These data, presented in table 3–4, shows an absence of childhood psychiatric symptomatology but a high incidence of conduct disturbances (almost 65 percent). Positive histories for

Table 3–4
Percent of Cluster A Cases and Total Study Sample Cases in Which Specific Childhood Behavior Abnormalities Were Present

Behavior Category	*Cluster A*[a] *(n = 20)*	*Total Sample*[b] *(n = 100)*
Any psychiatric symptoms	0.0	15.0
Speech disorders	0.0	0.0
Phobias	0.0	10.1
Sleep disturbances	0.0	4.0
Eating disturbances	0.0	4.0
Enuresis	0.0	2.0
Encopresis	0.0	0.0
Any disturbances of conduct	63.2	52.0
Fire setting	10.5	4.1
Cruelty to animals	15.8	5.2
Chronic lying	57.9	46.9
Repetitive stealing	47.4	42.9
Acts of vandalism	31.6	22.4
Any criminal behavior	45.0	40.0
Homicide	0.0	0.0
Rape	5.0	3.0
Other sexual crimes	10.0	4.0
Aggravated assault	25.0	13.0
Armed robbery	15.0	6.0
Other violent crimes	0.0	2.0
Property-related crimes	40.0	35.0
Drug-related crimes	5.0	17.0
Any school difficulties	70.0	74.0
Academic problems	70.0	68.0
Truancy problems	55.0	60.0
Any problems with relationships	94.7	92.0
School behavior problems	35.0	41.0
Violent behavior at school	20.0	10.0
Problems relating to father	84.2	82.7
Problems relating to mother	73.7	58.2
Problems relating to siblings	73.7	53.6
Difficulty making friends	68.4	59.2
Difficulty keeping friends	57.9	57.1
Repetitive temper outbursts	36.8	33.7
Chronic disobedience	57.9	46.9

[a]Some missing data for one case.
[b]Some missing data for two cases.

juvenile criminal behavior approach 50 percent. School and relationship difficulties are even more evident, with the latter almost universally present in this cluster. The absence of childhood psychiatric symptomatology is consonant with the absence of adult Axis I psychiatric disorders in the prototype. The high incidence of conduct disturbances and juvenile criminal behavior also are consonant with the antisocial behavior and high prevalence of Axis II personality disorders (especially antisocial personality disorders) observed in adulthood. The marked difficulties with relationships seen in almost every cluster A adult appear to be extensions of similar childhood and adolescent difficulties.

A Model of Cumulative Causation

Cluster A murderers lack the capacity to relate appropriately to other persons and have suffered this infirmity since childhood. Their behavior often is impulsive, almost always is exploitive, and becomes predatory when they are thwarted. Impulses of the moment are gratified without concern about consequences.

Cluster A murderers do not exhibit the symptoms or signs of Axis I psychiatric disorders such as psychoses or psychoneuroses, but they do occasionally manifest the symptoms of adult conduct disturbances. Cluster A murderers almost always exhibit behavior indicative of an Axis II personality disorder. Two such disorders predominate—antisocial personality disorder and borderline personality disorder—but other types also occur occasionally as well. The etiological roots of these disorders can be found in the conduct disturbances and juvenile criminal behavior of childhood.

Cluster A murderers lack socialization and behave in ways that indicate they espouse antisocial values. They often harbor a pervasive sense of alienation or disenfranchisement. They are quick to rationalize their homicidal acts or to engage in outright denials of responsibility.

Cluster A murderers also frequently exhibit significant histories of childhood trauma. More than half were exposed to negative role models. Many were exposed to physical abuse or neglect. More than half were removed from their familial environment and usually relocated in juvenile justice facilities.

Let us propose a paradigm for understanding the cumulative interaction of the core proximate causes that lead to homicidal behavior in this cluster. Other clusters provide corollaries for this paradigm, but the workings of the prototype provide a basic portrait of the homicide process. First, it must be noted that victims have little or no value to prototypical murderers. It is undoubtedly easier to destroy a devalued victim than one who is valued and with whom rewarding interactions can take place.

Second, the prototypical murderer's capacity and desire to moderate behavior, sometimes called impulse control, is lacking. In more intact individuals, activity is preceded by thoughtful deliberation, and impulses of the moment are stifled when they are inappropriate or would cause harm. This mechanism does not operate consistently, if at all, in cluster A murderers.

Third, internalized norms or values that are the product of socialization and that define the limits of acceptable behavior for more intact persons have not developed in cluster A murderers, who do not share socially sanctioned norms. This moral framework, which ordinarily would serve as a moderating influence or brake on behavior, is absent.

Fourth, cluster A murderers routinely engage in maladaptive behavior patterns that are the product of personality disorders. Such disorders introduce destructive, self-destructive, and self-defeating patterns of behavior that become the individual's characteristic way of acting. The cluster A murderer's repertoire for coping is limited and counterproductive.

Fifth, external constraints, which for other persons are connected to a fear of losing valued assets, privileges, or status, are lacking. Cluster A murderers feel alienated and/or disenfranchised and thus feel as though they have little or nothing to lose. Committing acts that may lead to dire consequences is easier when one feels that one is risking little or nothing. Feelings of alienation or disenfranchisement also lead to anger, bitterness, and resentment. This adds emotional fuel to the psychological fire that precedes a homicidal event.

Sixth, cluster A murderers perceive some rationalizing motive that appears to justify the direction of violence at a devalued target. Sometimes such motives act as a catalyst, and other times they simply justify the violence after it has occurred. Hence, the cause-and-effect status of this factor sometimes is hard to judge.

The outcome of this complex interaction of multiple factors is violence. The operant factors act in a mutually exacerbating and cumulative manner. One or two factors acting alone or in concert would be unlikely to induce a murderous result. However, as the number of proximate causes increases, the risk of such an outcome multiplies. A look at the cases in cluster A illustrates this point. All six of the proximate factors enumerated were present in six of the cases, and five factors were present in nine others (75 percent of the cluster). In two other cases, four factors were present, and in three cases, three factors were present. Note that none of the cases manifested fewer than three factors.

Also look at the factors that were most prevalent. In all but one of the twenty cases, the capacity for normal interpersonal relations was impaired, and in all but three cases, impulse control was lacking. Devaluation of the victim, coupled with inadequate control of behavior, are critical ingredients of homicide. Other proximate factors then trigger a conflagration or add fuel to the fire.

Our examination of other clusters will add important dimensions to the dynamics described here. In these other clusters, some of the factors described in this chapter are deemphasized, and others are given greater weight. Some factors disappear altogether, and others take their place. But the basic scenario is replayed, as variations on the theme.

4
Personality Dysfunction, Madness, and Homicide

The first variant of the prototype, cluster B, includes murderers who are even more dysfunctional than their prototype counterparts. Cluster B murderers share all of the prototype's core set of proximate causes and are afflicted by incapacitating psychiatric disorders in the form of psychoses. Cluster B constitutes as large a group as the prototype—20 percent of the total study population.

The Proximate Causal Pattern

Let us begin our discussion of this cluster with illustrative case examples.

> A.F., a forty-three-year-old unmarried male, killed a woman acquaintance. The victim's nude body was found in A.F.'s closet when the stench of the decomposing corpse caused the resident of an adjoining apartment to call the police. The victim had been stabbed with a knife that was covered with A.F.'s fingerprints. A.F.'s rambling utterances were never lucid enough to establish a motive, however, and he never acknowledged responsibility for the crime.
>
> Unable to tolerate relationships with anyone, A.F. had a history of exploitation at the hands of others who labeled him as "crazy" and exploited his limited assets. A.F. fumed with vitriolic anger toward his adoptive parents. These feelings were based on delusional beliefs of abuse. His life history was replete with impulsive and aggressive outbursts, several of which had led to criminal convictions. A.F. lived on the fringe of society, supported

by disability payments. He spent more time in prisons and psychiatric hospitals than in the community.

A.F. met the criteria for an Axis I diagnosis of schizophrenia and an Axis II diagnosis of antisocial personality disorder. The debilitating effects of the psychotic condition immeasurably increased his already great violence potential. A.F. manifested many long-standing symptoms of psychosis. His thought processes were marked by nonsensical thinking. He was extremely hard to understand and rambled in disconnected phrases. A.F. also expressed a number of long-standing delusional beliefs, insisting at times that he was John D. Rockefeller's son and at other times that he was Howard Hughes's son. He maintained that he had psychic powers and that he had been an intimate associate of Albert Einstein and Franklin Roosevelt. He reacted with intense hostility when questions were raised about any of these beliefs.

How A.F.'s beliefs may have contributed to his crime is hard to untangle, given his fragmented ability to communicate. It is possible that some incredulity on the part of his victim with respect to an expressed delusional belief precipitated the violent response. A.F. was one of two study subjects who was judged to be so impaired that he was permanently incompetent to stand trial.

J.X., a twenty-five–year–old unmarried male, had never demonstrated a capacity to function independently and had been supported throughout his adult life by his parents or disability benefits. J.X. killed three strangers and attempted to kill a fourth by bludgeoning them to death while they used urinals in public rest rooms. The crimes were committed several weeks apart—two in the same location and two in different locations. Too impaired to communicate intelligibly at the time of his arrest, he ultimately admitted responsibility for all four crimes.

J.X. described himself as a loner. His life was replete with instances of impulsive behavior and included repetitive acts of petty criminality. In contrast to A.F., J.X. had not engaged in prior criminal violence.

J.X. had no ties to the community and possessed no assets, skills, or future prospects. He met the criteria for diagnoses of both schizophrenia and antisocial personality disorder. The psychotic symptoms affected his behavior in profound ways, and the personality disorder set its antisocial tone. Among the psychotic symptoms were persecutory paranoid delusions, which contributed to J.X.'s state of chronic anxiety. He believed that he was being followed by creatures from outer space who had implanted a metal device in his ear through which instructions were transmitted. J.X.'s thinking was so fragmented that at the time of his arrest, he was communicating in "word salad," sequences of words and syllables that were utterly incomprehensible to the listener.

J.X.'s case demonstrated a more specific link between psychosis and the homicidal behavior than could be established in A.F.'s case. The auditory hallucinations that J.X. perceived provided this link. These "voices" called him vile names and issued commands instructing him to commit the homicidal acts and threatening him with death if he failed to comply. Tortured by these unceasing hallucinations, J.X. resisted for as long as he could but ultimately acted to comply. Each homicidal event provided only transient relief, as the voices always demanded additional violence.

K.H., twenty-five years of age and unmarried, was not gainfully employed at the time of his arrest and had been supported for years by family members and friends and by educational grants, loans, and occasional part-time jobs. K.H. had a prior history of convictions for a potpourri of criminal offenses, including assault, drunk driving, and possession of illicit drugs. He ultimately strangled to death his recently estranged girlfriend. The relationship had been highly volatile, and the victim had recently ended it to pursue a new one. K.H. initially claimed not to recall his crime but finally did acknowledge it.

K.H. was a loner, a man with few friends who had

developed a profound dependence on his victim. A history of impulsive behavior was manifested primarily by poor educational and occupational decisions, which left K.H. bereft of opportunities. Plagued by these decisions, he came to feel alienated and cheated but rationalized his misfortunes as the effects of racism, failing to acknowledge any responsibility as a consequence of his lackadaisical efforts. K.H.'s prior criminal history, a combination of violent and nonviolent offenses, demonstrated his antisocial inclinations.

K.H.'s irrational response to the loss of a relationship appears to have precipitated his crime. His victim was insistent on ending the relationship, and K.H. reacted with violence. His extreme response can be linked to his antisocial attitudes, his sense of alienation, and the effects of psychosis, exacerbated by the use of phencyclidine (PCP) and alcohol just prior to the crime.

K.H.'s psychotic symptoms necessitated two psychiatric hospitalizations in the three-week period prior to the crime. Delusional, K.H. believed himself to be the victim of a Mafia plot to infiltrate the Central Intelligence Agency (CIA). He expressed a second delusional belief that electromagnetic waves could bring dead people back to life, a belief that may well have enabled K.H. to kill someone on whom he was emotionally dependent. He also reported visual and auditory hallucinations during the same period.

While K.H.'s recollection of his crime was vague and incomplete, it is likely that his delusional thinking, worsened by the effects of PCP and alcohol and linked to his anger over having been rejected by a "racist" girlfriend, acted together to induce the homicidal act.

D.A., thirty-seven years of age, Caucasian, and twice divorced, was living with a girlfriend when he shot and killed a black stranger whom he observed talking to a white woman. Family members, friends, and coworkers described D.A. as a man who harbored intense racial hatred and a belief that white women were being tricked, intimidated, and victimized by black men. D.A. freely acknowledged responsibility for his crime but would not discuss his motives and denied racist beliefs.

D.A. was an isolated, angry man whose relationships were invariably problematic. He married unsuccessfully twice and at the time of his crime was living with a girlfriend in a volatile and hostile relationship.

D.A.'s antisocial inclinations were evidenced by a prior conviction for armed robbery and a period of reincarceration for a parole violation. Despite having earned a high school diploma and having completed two years of college course work, D.A. was employed as a dishwasher and expressed feelings of both alienation and disenfranchisement.

D.A.'s case illustrates how paranoid delusions can affect behavior. D.A. harbored a fixed delusional belief that God had empowered him to kill black men because they were co-opting white women into sexual subservience. He also believed himself to be in constant jeopardy and was known to sleep on his roof armed with a gun to protect himself from his black enemies. D.A.'s crime was directly attributable to his delusional beliefs. Although he was unwilling to discuss these beliefs with me, he had verbalized them many times to others to whom I spoke.

L.B., thirty years of age, once divorced, and once widowed, was supported by welfare payments at the time of her arrest and had never been gainfully employed. L.B. had approached several community agencies with complaints of having been victimized, but these complaints could never be substantiated.

L.B.'s past relationships were chaotic, as evidenced by a long procession of husbands and boyfriends. The chaos was such that one of her boyfriends killed one of her husbands. Prior to her crime, L.B. had a long history of petty criminality and impulsive violence, the latter often unprovoked and only sometimes related to delusional beliefs. L.B.'s expressed feelings of alienation, which she attributed to racial discrimination, were aggravated by what she perceived to be a lack of responsiveness on the part of community agencies.

L.B.'s case illustrates how a festering delusion of persecution can result in homicide. L.B. and her victim, a neighbor, had quarreled intermittently for several years. She accused him of harboring racist attitudes. She failed to perceive that the chaos in her life, the violent arguments, the loud all-night parties, and the yard strewn with trash and abandoned cars may have contributed to her neighbor's ill will. Multiple appeals to the police by L.B. failed to achieve the sanctions she sought against this neighbor. Just prior to the crime, L.B. came to believe that the neighbor was spying on her and had surreptitiously entered her home to steal her possessions.

When the police failed to substantiate her claim, L.B. took matters into her own hands. When she spotted the neighbor outside his home, she attacked him with a rock. He later died in the hospital.

L.B.'s active psychosis had been amply documented by the local community mental health system. Records from these contacts indicated irrational and illogical thinking, rambling nonsensical communications, and persecutory delusional beliefs. L.B.'s homicidal act appears to have been precipitated by a worsening of her psychotic symptoms. L.B.'s antisocial history was documented by criminal justice system records, which indicated a range of dishonest behaviors over many years.

The case illustrations presented here can be augmented with a quantitative assessment of cluster B's proximate causal profile. The data needed to do this are presented in table 4–1. The data in this table indicate that few areas of function were unaffected in this cluster. Even the factor least often affected, cognition, was impaired in 30 percent of the cases. Rates for impaired self-image, substance abuse problems, and intoxication equalled or exceeded 40 percent. All other factors demonstrated even higher impairment rates.

Also presented in table 4–1 are comparative data for the prototype cluster. Cluster B cases can be distinguished from the

Table 4–1
Percent of Cluster B Cases and Prototype Cases in Which Specific Proximate Causal Factors Were Present

Proximate Cause Category	*Cluster B (n = 20)*	*Prototype (n = 20)*
Baseline mental functions		
Impaired interpersonal relations	90.0	95.0
Impaired impulse control	85.0	85.0
Impaired reality testing	75.0	0.0
Impaired thinking	80.0	5.0
Impaired cognition	30.0	5.0
Impaired self-image	45.0	5.0
Antisocial values	75.0	75.0
Alienation/disenfranchisement	100.0	75.0
Presence of Axis I symptomatic psychiatric disorders		
Psychoses	100.0	0.0
Psychoneuroses	0.0	5.0
Substance abuse disorders	0.0	0.0
Behavior/organic/mental retardation	0.0	25.0
No Axis I disorder	0.0	70.0
Presence of Axis II personality disorders		
Antisocial personality	30.0	50.0
Borderline, paranoid, schizoid, or schizotypal personality	30.0	35.0
Histrionic or narcissistic personality	0.0	5.0
Low-impact disorders (avoidant, dependent, obsessive-compulsive, or passive-aggressive)	15.0	0.0
No Axis II disorder	25.0	10.0
Presence of substance abuse problems (with or without diagnosis of substance abuse disorder)		
Alcohol abuse only	10.0	5.0
Drug abuse only	10.0	5.0
Both alcohol and drug abuse	20.0	10.0
Presence of transient factors		
Rationalizing or justifying motives	70.0	70.0
Intoxication	45.0	5.0
Significant stress	60.0	40.0

prototype by the presence of psychotic disorders and related impairment of two baseline mental functions, reality testing and rational thinking. Also notable in this cluster are the more diverse array of personality disorders and the higher proportion of cases without any personality disorder.

Cluster B murderers were less likely than protoptypical murderers to deny responsibility for their crimes. They expressed rationalizing motives as frequently as did prototypical murderers, but the content of their motives was different. Cluster B murderers were likely to claim that they were reacting to some threat to their person, but in every instance the threat had its origin in a psychotic delusion. Prototypical murderers also sometimes claimed self-defense, but those claims were clearly lies. Neither conflicts over money nor homicidal acts committed in conjunction with other felonies were relevant motives in cluster B as they were in the prototype.

Taking both the case examples and the quantitative data into account, the twenty cases in cluster B share the following common pattern of proximate causes with the prototype:

1. Almost all exhibited impairment of interpersonal relations and impulse control.
2. Most met the criteria for the diagnosis of an Axis II personality disorder.
3. In many cases, a failure of socialization and the presence of antisocial values were noted.
4. All expressed a long-standing sense of alienation and/or disenfranchisement.
5. Many offered some rationalizing motive for their crimes, but these motives differed in context from those expressed by the prototypical murderers.

Cluster B murderers differ from the prototype in the following respects:

1. All met the criteria for the diagnosis of an Axis I psychotic disorder.
2. Most exhibited impairment of reality testing and rational thinking.
3. Intoxication, impaired self-image, and stress, were not predominant factors but were commonly present.

This is the constellation of proximate factors that provides cluster B with its basic identity.

The Demographic Pattern

An examination of cluster B's demographic pattern yields a profile that is strikingly different from that of the prototype in several important respects. These comparisons are presented in table 4–2. Note the much higher proportion of women murderers in cluster B. As we will see when we examine cluster F, women rarely murder unless they are psychotic. Also striking is the absence of complex crimes in cluster B in contrast to the prototype, where the incidence of such cases was 35 percent. Cluster B murderers are somewhat less predatory than their prototype counterparts and suffer from psychiatric disorders, which means that they often lack the mental capacities necessary to plan and implement complex acts.

Table 4–2

Percent of Cluster B Cases and Prototype Cases in Which Specific Demographic Characteristics Were Present

Demographic Category	*Cluster B (n = 20)*	*Prototype (n = 20)*
Assailant is male	75.0	90.0
Assailant is female	25.0	10.0
Assailant has prior criminal convictions	60.0	65.0
Assailant has no prior criminal convictions	40.0	35.0
Victim is known to assailant	80.0	70.0
Victim is not known to assailant	20.0	30.0
Assailant committed homicide only	100.0	65.0
Assailant committed homicide and rape	0.0	25.0
Assailant committed homicide and robbery	0.0	10.0
Assailant is younger than 18 years old	5.0	5.0
Assailant is 18 to 24 years old	15.0	25.0
Assailant is 25 to 39 years old	50.0	50.0
Assailant is 40 years or older	30.0	20.0
Assailant killed only one victim	80.0	70.0
Assailant killed more than one victim	20.0	30.0

The Long-Term Causal and Childhood Behavior Patterns

To examine cluster B from the perspectives of long-term causal patterns and childhood behavior patterns, it is necessary to add information to each of the case illustrations.

> A.F. was abandoned by his natural parents at birth, necessitating institutionalization until age four, when he was adopted. He experienced chronic difficulties adapting to his adoptive home, but there was no evidence that these difficulties were a consequence of parental abuse or neglect. Neither the adoptive parents nor their natural children presented negative role models. None of A.F.'s adoptive siblings has experienced difficulties in adulthood.
>
> A.F.'s childhood was disrupted by several periods of incarceration in juvenile facilities for both assault and burglary offenses. His childhood history was replete with behavioral difficulties, including frequent temper tantrums, chronic disobedience, lying, stealing, and academic and truancy problems. A.F. could not get along well with teachers, peers, or family members. By all indications, he was an exceedingly strange child whose growth and development patterns always deviated from normal expectations.

In contrast to A.F., J.X. was brought up by his natural parents. Like A.F., J.X.'s three male siblings have led trouble-free lives. J.X.'s father cooperated fully with the evaluative process, but his mother, who was described by other family members as reclusive and eccentric, refused to participate at all, raising the possibility that she was psychiatrically impaired. No definite evidence of physical or sexual abuse or neglect was discovered, but several family members intimated that the father administered harsh corporal punishment to J.X. in response to chronic misbehavior.

J.X. exhibited conduct disturbances very similar to those of A.F., but unlike A.F., he amassed no record of serious juvenile criminal offenses. Psychiatric distress during childhood took the form of chronic extreme fears, which exceeded normal developmental expectations. J.X.'s father recalled that J.X. was different from all the other children, but he could not articulate the specific nature of the differences.

K.H., like J.X., came from an intact family but one in which neither parent appears to have been impaired or antisocial. An older sibling who served as a role model for K.H. did, however, exhibit drug abuse problems. Some instability in K.H.'s upbringing resulted from his father's status as a career soldier, which necessitated frequent family moves.

In contrast to both A.F. and J.X., K.H. had a childhood history that was surprisingly unremarkable except for some problems with substance abuse during adolescence and erratic academic performance. Additionally, K.H. was quite shy and experienced marked difficulties establishing and maintaining friendships.

D.A. also grew up in an intact family. So far as could be determined, his rabid racist attitudes were not learned or reinforced in the family home, but it is not likely that D.A.'s parents would have confirmed this had it occurred. The overt communications of family members disavowed D.A.'s racist attitudes. No traumatic childhood experiences were discovered in this case.

D.A. exhibited a typical prepsychotic childhood history. He was described by his parents as an inordinately fearful child. He was quiet and isolated, a loner who kept to himself and made no friends. A marginally average student academically, D.A. exhibited behavior problems at school. He did not, however, commit any juvenile offenses.

L.B. came from a broken home. Her alcoholic father died during her childhood, and a less than adequate mother chronically neglected her. She had no positive role models to emulate, and a profound sense of insecurity reigned throughout her childhood. There was no evidence of sexual or physical abuse, however, and L.B. was not removed from her childhood home despite its inadequacies.

L.B. began to exhibit psychotic symptoms during late adolescence. She denied earlier psychiatric symptoms, a contention that could not be refuted by other available information, although it is conceivable that such findings were present but not recorded. Disturbances of conduct were not reported during childhood or adolescence.

These case illustrations suggest that cluster B murderers were raised in more stable circumstances than were their prototype

Table 4–3

Percent of Cluster B Cases and Prototype Cases in Which Specific Long-Term Causal Factors Were Present

Long-Term Cause Category	*Cluster B*[a] *(n = 20)*	*Prototype*[b] *(n = 20)*
Any negative role models	44.4	55.6
Father had criminal history	5.6	17.6
Father had substance abuse problems	16.7	11.8
Mother had criminal history	0.0	5.3
Mother had substance abuse problems	5.3	26.3
Sibling had criminal history	5.3	31.6
Sibling had substance abuse problems	21.1	36.8
Any instability in childhood environment	61.1	72.2
One parent absent	55.0	68.4
Both parents absent	25.0	10.5
One or both parents died	10.5	5.3
One or more siblings died	5.3	0.0
Father was mentally ill	16.7	5.6
Mother was mentally ill	15.8	10.5
Sibling was mentally ill	15.8	5.3
Parents were divorced	31.6	63.2
Any lack of safety in childhood environment	60.0	73.7
Exposure to physical abuse	35.0	36.8
Exposure to sexual abuse	10.0	5.3
Exposure to pervasive neglect	60.0	63.2
Any disruption in childhood environment	35.0	52.6
Placement in institutional setting	35.0	47.4
Hospitalization in medical setting	5.0	10.5
Hospitalization in psychiatric setting	10.0	10.5

[a]Some missing data for two cases.
[b]Some missing data for three cases.

counterparts. A quantitative analysis of long-term causal factors in this cluster (table 4–3) only partially supports this observation. It does reveal a lower overall incidence of trauma than was found in the prototype. The incidence of trauma exceeds 50 percent in only two of four subcategories—instability in the childhood environment and a lack of safety in that environment. While these incidence rates are lower than those of the prototype, they are still quite high.

It is possible to explain the homicidal behavior of cluster B murderers despite the lower incidence rates of trauma. A substantial body of evidence points to a genetic contribution to the etiology of psychosis. Given such a genetic contribution, it is likely that less environmental trauma is necessary to produce the same homicidal outcome.

The childhood behavior patterns depicted in the cluster B case illustrations were more likely to include both psychiatric symptoms and conduct disturbances than were those observed in the prototype. In one of the cases, psychotic symptoms were already in evidence during adolescence. In others, prepsychotic symptoms took the form of extreme fears and self-imposed isolation. Academic difficulties also were very common. In most of these cases, a prediction of future psychiatric disability would not have been difficult to make.

A quantitative analysis of childhood behavior patterns (table 4–4) corroborates these differences between cluster B and the prototype. The two clusters do not differ appreciably with respect to measures such as juvenile criminality, school difficulties, and problems with relationships. When conduct disturbances are examined, however, cluster B murderers demonstrate a lower incidence rate than the prototype. Conversely, when psychiatric symptomatology is examined, cluster B murderers demonstrate a substantial incidence rate that is nonexistent in the prototype. These rates appear to predict the adult distinctions that can be made between the two clusters.

Psychotic Symptomatology and Homicidal Behavior

Now let us examine the salient features that categorize cluster B murderers, highlighting those characteristics that distinguish clus-

Table 4–4
Percent of Cluster B Cases and Prototype Cases in Which Specific Childhood Behavior Abnormalities Were Present

Behavior Category	*Cluster B (n = 20)*	*Prototype[a] (n = 20)*
Any psychiatric symptoms	35.0	0.0
Speech disorders	0.0	0.0
Phobias	30.0	0.0
Sleep disturbances	5.0	0.0
Eating disturbances	0.0	0.0
Enuresis	0.0	0.0
Encopresis	0.0	0.0
Any disturbances of conduct	50.0	63.2
Fire setting	5.0	10.5
Cruelty to animals	5.0	15.8
Chronic lying	35.0	57.9
Repetitive stealing	50.0	47.4
Acts of vandalism	20.0	31.6
Any criminal behavior	40.0	45.0
Homicide	0.0	0.0
Rape	0.0	5.0
Other sexual crimes	0.0	10.0
Aggravated assault	15.0	25.0
Armed robbery	0.0	15.0
Other violent crimes	0.0	0.0
Property-related crimes	40.0	40.0
Drug-related crimes	20.0	5.0
Any school difficulties	70.0	70.0
Academic problems	65.0	70.0
Truancy problems	45.0	55.0
Any problems with relationships	94.7	94.7
School behavior problems	35.0	35.0
Violent behavior at school	10.0	20.0
Problems relating to father	80.0	84.2
Problems relating to mother	50.0	73.7
Problems relating to siblings	42.1	73.7
Difficulty making friends	80.0	68.4
Difficulty keeping friends	75.0	57.9
Repetitive temper outbursts	35.0	36.8
Chronic disobedience	35.0	57.9

[a]Some missing data for one case.

ter B from the prototype. Cluster B cases add to the prototype's core set of proximate factors and thus can be expected to fit the paradigm outlined in chapter 3.

Cluster B and the prototype share difficulties in establishing and maintaining interpersonal relationships and controlling impulses. A sense of alienation and/or disenfranchisement also is present in both groups. Diagnoses of personality disorders are common in both groups, although a more diverse range of such disorders is noted in cluster B. Both groups exhibit behavior indicative of antisocial values, but cluster B murderers appear to be somewhat less predatory. In both clusters, rationalizing motives usually are present, but those expounded by cluster B murderers tend to be more delusional and less self-serving.

The singularly most striking difference between cluster B and the prototype concerns the universal presence in cluster B of psychotic disorders. Most prototypical murderers exhibited no Axis I disorders, and the few who did usually manifested conduct disturbances or organic disorders rather than psychotic disorders. Cluster B reveals a profoundly different picture in which psychotic disorders were diagnosed in every case.

Psychotic disorders impair the capacity to perceive one's environment accurately and to react appropriately to its demands. Consider for a moment an individual who believes herself to be in mortal danger and who concludes that she must strike before her enemies destroy her. Consider next that the belief is delusional and has no basis in reality. Such paranoid delusions often are powerful enough to overwhelm residual rational judgment and provide a compelling reason to react in some ill-considered (violent) way. J.X. and D.A. both believed themselves to be in danger, and L.B. believed that she was the victim of persecution. All reacted to their beliefs and used psychotically impaired mental mechanisms to respond to the perceived threats.

Thought is sometimes referred to as trial action. Thinking through a situation enables an individual to consider, or mentally try out, different options before committing to a particular course of action. When the capacity to think has been fragmented, trial action ceases to play a role, and behavior becomes impulsive. Consider the fragmented thinking in all the case illustrations in relation to the murderers' decisions to act violently.

Psychoses also can distort perceptions. The hallucinatory phenomena that occur frequently in psychoses create such distortions. Hallucinations usually are auditory or visual. Auditory hallucinations, the "voices" that psychotic individuals perceive, introduce false information or torment their victims with threats or criticisms. In the case of command hallucinations, the voices issue instructions with regard to behavior. This is illustrated in the case of J.X., whose command hallucinations instructed him to kill his victims or risk his own demise. While some psychotic individuals are able to recognize the illusory nature of hallucinations, many others cannot and accept them as reality. The response to such misperceived reality may take the form of violence.

In summary, when we examine cluster B murderers, all of the prototype's disabilities are in evidence. In addition, impaired reality testing, fragmented thinking, and the impact of delusions and hallucinations take their toll. The exploitive and predatory interpersonal behaviors so characteristic of the prototype are less evident in cluster B murderers, who tend to be more isolated and detached from others. Precipitating motives are present in both clusters, but cluster B motives usually are more rooted in delusions. With respect to long-term causal factors, cluster B murderers suffer traumas similar to those suffered by prototype murderers, albeit less frequently. Demographically, cluster B murderers differ from their prototype counterparts in that assailants do not commit complex crimes and more frequently are women. Cluster B murderers are more likely to have suffered from psychiatric symptoms and somewhat less likely to have exhibited conduct disturbances during childhood. As we will see later, these differences have important implications for both prevention and treatment.

5
Personality Dysfunction, Psychoneurosis, Impaired Self-Image, Stress, and Homicide

The second variant of the prototype cluster, cluster C, comprises murderers who share most of the prototype's proximate causes but also are impaired by the debilitating effects of psychoneurotic disorders, an impoverished sense of self-esteem, and exposure to significant stress. Although psychoneuroses are not usually associated with levels of dysfunction as debilitating as those seen with psychotic disorders, their impact can be pronounced especially when combined with exposure to stress and impaired self-esteem.

Cluster C does not comprise as many cases as clusters A or B and accounts for only 13 percent of the total study population. Together the three clusters account for more than half of the entire sample.

The Proximate Causal Pattern

Let us begin by presenting some illustrative case examples.

> At the time of his crime, B.H., a forty-two–year–old male, was living apart from his estranged wife, a woman to whom he had been married twice. B.H. killed a long-time friend who was also his attorney by emptying the chambers of two handguns into the victim's body. B.H. alleged that the victim swindled him out of tens of thou-

sands of dollars over a period of several years. The homicidal act occurred after B.H. allegedly pleaded with his victim to make restitution and, according to B.H., the victim responded with ridicule.

B.H.'s case provides a good example of a chronically depressed man whose personality impairments were severe enough to induce profound passivity and perpetual acquiescence to exploitation by others. His diminished sense of self-esteem and exposure to multiple stresses finally led to a violent outburst.

While B.H. had no prior criminal history, he did have a history of repetitive, highly dependent, and naively trusting relationships with other people. He often would ignore evidence of exploitation, however obvious, in his desire to avoid disagreements. For example, B.H.'s estranged wife described how he turned a blind eye to her obvious infidelities until they could no longer be ignored. Even then, B.H. could not express his anger until intoxicated.

B.H. met the criteria for a diagnosis of neurotic depression, including episodes of despondency, withdrawal, loss of interest in ordinarily pleasurable activities, crying spells, insomnia, and anorexia. B.H. verbalized suicidal ideation periodically but had acted on it only once, some years earlier when he consumed an overdose of an over-the-counter sleeping medication. He also suffered from a long-standing dependence on alcohol.

B.H. was diagnosed as suffering from an Axis II dependent personality disorder, given his pervasive tendency to relinquish adult responsibilities to others and to subordinate his needs to theirs. He demonstrated a profound lack of self-confidence and articulated a marked sense of inferiority.

While B.H. exhibited a sense of disenfranchisement, this was quite recent in origin and was directly related to his economic losses. He had accumulated considerable assets before losing almost everything he owned.

B.H.'s perception of being exploited and humiliated at the hands of his victim was only one of multiple ongoing stresses in his life. A physical injury suffered shortly before the crime left B.H. feeling that he was less capable of supporting himself. At the same time, his work performance, always the primary source of whatever self-esteem he did enjoy, was derided by a new supervisor. This criticism was reinforced by the outcome of a continuing education course he attended in which he received an uncharacteristically low grade. Additionally, the self-esteem he had garnered from participation in a blood donor program six times a year was summarily terminated when B.H. tested positive for hepatitis. The combined effect of these stresses played havoc with B.H.'s self-esteem, which was already impaired as a consequence of childhood experiences to be examined later.

B.H.'s victim served as both a direct and a symbolic target for accumulated frustrations and resentments. The victim's alleged ridiculing triggered the outburst of pent-up rage that culminated in violence. After the crime, B.H. wandered off in a confused daze that dissipated quickly, at which point he turned himself in to the police. B.H. maintained throughout the judicial process that he should be punished harshly for what he had done.

N.M., fifty-six years of age and divorced, killed his ex-wife and her father and wounded her mother in a single outburst of violence. He shot the two women in the ex-wife's driveway after stopping to exchange insults. N.M. then proceeded to his ex–father-in-law's home and killed him. He then searched for his ex-wife's divorce attorney but could not find the man. Retiring to a motel where he tried to muster the "resolve" to take his own life, N.M. finally called the police.

The case of N.M. provides a good example of an embittered man whose coping skills were weakened by the combined effects of chronic personality dysfunctions, psychiatric illness, stress, and intoxication. With judgment impaired, he externalized blame for his circumstances onto others and reacted with violence.

N.M. exhibited a chronic lack of success in marriage,

which ended in divorce, leaving him lonely and bitter and feeling alienated from his children. The latter occurred because of his unreasonable demands that the children take his side in the marital dispute, a demand they rejected. After the divorce, N.M.'s subsequent relationships fared little better. On the day of the crime, a girlfriend terminated the most recent of these relationships because she could no longer tolerate N.M.'s frequent onslaughts of verbal abuse.

At the same time, N.M. was experiencing symptoms of depression, including despondency, crying spells, nightmares, and withdrawal from normal activities. These symptoms depleted his already marginal coping skills. N.M.'s history of unstable but intense relationships, frequent mood swings, self-destructive behavior, and inordinate intolerance of being alone all supported an Axis II diagnosis of borderline personality disorder.

N.M. felt both alienated and disenfranchised, the consequence of a divorce settlement that left him economically depleted after an interminable series of legal battles. N.M. blamed this outcome on his ex-wife's "scheming parents and crooked lawyer."

On the day of the crime, the loss of yet another relationship exacerbated N.M.'s sense of isolation and failure. On his way home from that encounter, already angry and intoxicated, N.M. passed his ex-wife's home, and their fatal interaction began. N.M. claims that his ex-wife reached into her car, causing him to conclude erroneously that she was reaching for a gun. He then reached for the gun he kept in his glove compartment and commenced firing. The binge of violence described above began.

R.D., a twenty-three–year–old married male, became preoccupied with a young, attractive woman neighbor who, according to R.D., had visits from many men at odd hours. R.D. experienced a myriad of erotic thoughts about this woman, including daydreams in which she willingly submitted to his sexual whims. As these fantasies intensified, he surreptitiously entered her home while she was away and obtained her name, phone number, and a pair of her panties. Next he made a series of sexually explicit phone calls to the woman expressing his desire for sexual dominance over her. R.D. believed that the woman was interested and aroused by the calls. After several weeks, R.D. arranged to visit the woman in her home. When he arrived there, he was confronted by an armed man who R.D. erroneously concluded was an angry husband or boyfriend. A struggle ensued, R.D. gained control of the weapon, and the man, who was a police officer, was killed. R.D. fled the scene but was taken into custody soon thereafter. He acknowledged responsibility for the crime but stated that he had acted because he felt himself to be in mortal danger.

R.D. manifested a long history of impaired relationships. He had few male friends, and his relationships with women, including his wife, were marked by neurotic struggles revolving around the issue of dominance and submission. R.D. was plagued by feelings of inferiority and inadequacy and attempted to balance these with fantasies of domination over women. When he attempted to act out these fantasies in the context of his marital relationship, his wife resisted, and this failure left him feeling even more inadequate. In the marriage, R.D. did exhibit several losses of control during which he struck his wife.

At the time of the crime, R.D. was suffering from a mixed psychoneurotic disorder marked by symptoms of anxiety, obsessional thinking, compulsive behavior, and despondency. There also were indications of marked psychosexual confusion. R.D. recognized the inappropriateness of his escalating sexual preoccupation with the neighbor but admitted that he could not control his thoughts or behavior. R.D.'s angry intolerance of other points of view, his rigidity, and his pronounced inability to express warmth or tenderness toward others indicated an Axis II diagnosis of compulsive personality disorder. When R.D. finally went to the woman's home and encountered the victim, his already impaired coping skills failed completely, and he reacted with violence.

The pattern of proximate causes illustrated by these case examples suggests that the cluster C cases were beset by both personality dysfunctions and psychoneuroses. Significant stresses almost always were present, as were rationalizing motives. Substance abuse and intoxication at times acted as aggravating or precipitating factors. This pattern is corroborated by the quantitative analysis of the cluster C cases (table 5–1). Impairment of

Table 5–1
Percent of Cluster C Cases and Prototype Cases in Which Specific Proximate Causal Factors Were Present

Proximate Cause Category	*Cluster C (n = 13)*	*Prototype (n = 20)*
Baseline mental functions		
Impaired interpersonal relations	84.6	95.0
Impaired impulse control	84.6	85.0
Impaired reality testing	0.0	0.0
Impaired thinking	23.1	5.0
Impaired cognition	7.7	5.0
Impaired self-image	92.3	5.0
Antisocial values	46.2	75.0
Alienation/disenfranchisement	76.9	75.0
Presence of Axis I symptomatic psychiatric disorders		
Psychoses	0.0	0.0
Psychoneuroses	92.3	5.0
Substance abuse disorders	7.7	0.0
Behavior/organic/mental retardation	0.0	25.0
No Axis I disorder	0.0	70.0
Presence of Axis II personality disorders		
Antisocial personality	23.1	50.0
Borderline, paranoid, schizoid, or schizotypal personality	23.1	35.0
Histrionic or narcissistic personality	7.7	5.0
Low impact disorders (avoidant, dependent, obsessive-compulsive, or passive-aggressive)	30.8	0.0
No Axis II disorder	15.4	10.0
Presence of substance abuse problems (with or without diagnosis of substance abuse disorder)		
Alcohol abuse only	30.8	5.0
Drug abuse only	7.7	5.0
Both alcohol and drug abuse	23.1	10.0
Presence of transient factors		
Rationalizing or justifying motives	84.6	70.0
Intoxication	53.8	5.0
Significant stress	92.3	40.0

two baseline personality functions, interpersonal relations and impulse control, occurred in all but two cases. Feelings of alienation and/or disenfranchisement were common, although, unlike the prototype, they were quite recent in origin. In this cluster, ties to the community were lost, often in temporal proximity to the homicidal event. The cluster C murderers usually blamed their victims for this loss.

In addition, impaired self-image was almost universal in these murderers. Psychoneurotic disorders were present in all but one cluster C case. Both of these factors were almost unknown in the prototypical murderers. Cluster C cases usually met the criteria for a diagnosis of some kind of personality disorder, but antisocial personality disorders, which were common in the prototype, were less common here, and low-impact disorders, unknown in the prototype, were common in this cluster.

Exposure to significant stress was a prominent factor in all but one case. Substance abuse problems were present 60 percent of the time, and intoxication was present in half of the cases. Rationalizing motives were almost always present, and romantic disputes, quarrels over money, and revenge motives predominated. This is in contrast to both the prototype, in which denials of responsibility and self-serving rationalizations were prominent, and cluster B, in which delusional motives predominated. Only one cluster C murderer denied responsibility for his crime. As a group, the cluster C murderers were less antisocial than their prototype counterparts and perceived themselves to have been exploited by their victims.

Taking all of the above into account, cluster C shares the following proximate causal pattern in common with the prototype:

1. Almost all exhibited impairments of interpersonal relations and impulse control.

2. Almost all met the criteria for the diagnosis of an Axis II personality disorder, although the types of disorders exhibited differed somewhat from those exhibited by the prototype.

3. Almost all offered some rationalizing motive for their crimes, although the nature of these motives differed from those expressed by prototypical murderers.

4. Most expressed a sense of alienation and/or disenfranchisement, although in contrast to the prototype, these feelings were recent in origin and usually had some specific link to the victim.

Cluster C differs from the prototype in the following ways:

1. Almost all met the criteria for the diagnosis of an Axis I psychoneurotic disorder.
2. Almost all demonstrated an impoverished sense of self-image.
3. Almost all demonstrated exposure to significant and pervasive stress.

This is the basic profile that identifies cluster C murderers.

The Demographic Pattern

Cluster C's demographic pattern, which is consonant with its proximate causal pattern, is presented in table 5–2. Notable is

Table 5–2
Precent of Cluster C Cases and Prototype Cases in Which Specific Demographic Characteristics Were Present

Demographic Category	*Cluster C (n = 13)*	*Prototype (n = 20)*
Assailant is male	100.0	90.0
Assailant is female	0.0	10.0
Assailant has prior criminal convictions	38.5	65.0
Assailant has no prior criminal convictions	61.5	35.0
Victim is known to assailant	84.6	70.0
Victim is not known to assailant	15.4	30.0
Assailant committed homicide only	100.0	65.0
Assailant committed homicide and rape	0.0	25.0
Assailant committed homicide and robbery	0.0	10.0
Assailant is younger than 18 years old	15.4	5.0
Assailant is 18 to 24 years old	15.4	25.0
Assailant is 25 to 39 years old	46.2	50.0
Assailant is 40 years or older	23.1	20.0
Assailant killed only one victim	61.5	70.0
Assailant killed more than one victim	38.5	30.0

the absence of women, not surprising in a cluster that has no association with psychotic disorders. Relatively few cluster C murderers had prior criminal histories, and none committed complex crimes such as homicide and rape or homicide and robbery. These findings are compatible with the less antisocial orientation of this cluster as compared to the prototype and cluster B.

The Long-Term Causal and Childhood Behavior Patterns

To explore the patterns of long-term causality and childhood behavior in this cluster, let us add to what is already known about each of the case examples.

> B.H. was raised by an alcoholic father whom he had to nurse through numerous alcoholic binges. B.H.'s mother ran off with a boyfriend when B.H. was only nine years of age, and there is evidence to suggest that she physically abused B.H. before her departure. The father, when sober, was invariably critical of B.H., which helps to explain B.H.'s abysmally low self-esteem in adulthood. Gross neglect on the part of the father and abandonment by the mother engendered a festering rage that B.H. went to great lengths to conceal from himself and others. The father's alcoholism contributed a negative role model that B.H. emulated as an adult.
>
> These were not the only traumas in B.H.'s childhood. He spent several months hospitalized in a state of quadriplegic paralysis at the age of two from an illness that remitted spontaneously. One can imagine the terror that such an illness would provoke in a young child.
>
> Psychiatric symptoms also were evident during childhood. These included sleep and eating disturbances. B.H. was described as an isolated child who kept to himself and made no close ties to friends or siblings. He did not exhibit conduct disturbances, juvenile criminal behavior, or school difficulties. He graduated from high school and later completed a series of technical courses in electronics, the field in which he was working at the time of his crime.

In contrast to B.H., N.M. grew up in an intact family. No special problems were reported, and no evidence of abuse or neglect could be documented. If traumatic events did occur in N.M.'s childhood, they escaped detection by public agencies and were not revealed during the evaluative process by N.M. or by members of his family.

According to N.M.'s own account and that of his parents, he experienced no childhood psychiatric symptoms and exhibited no juvenile criminal behavior or conduct disturbances. While all parties involved may have been minimizing antecedent difficulties, no documented evidence of such difficulties could be found in school or other public records. N.M. completed high school and college and was working in a managerial position at the time of his crime.

R.D. came from a childhood environment that was neither as deprived as that of B.H. nor as apparently normal as that of N.M. R.D. described his father as an unreliable womanizer. He was aware of his father's infidelities and was forced by the father to play a conspiratorial role in them. The parents divorced when R.D. was sixteen years of age, and thereafter contact with the father was markedly diminished. The divorce precipitated R.D.'s depressive symptomatology and academic and behavior problems at school. His mother, the parent with whom he lived, was preoccupied with her own problems and did not intervene. Subsequently, this problematic child was shuttled back and forth between the parents, neither of whom appeared to be interested in his care.

R.D.'s academic and truancy problems were so severe that he was forced to repeat the eleventh grade, but he ultimately did graduate from high school. Seemingly unable to make friends and an only child, he remained isolated. R.D. did not commit any juvenile criminal offenses. After completing high school, he accepted a low-paying job in a landscaping business, a position he held at the time of his crime.

These case examples provide a mixed picture of childhood trauma and deprivation. A quantitative analysis of long-term causes for all thirteen cases in cluster C is presented in table 5–3. This analysis suggests that trauma was as much in evidence among the cluster C murderers as it was among the prototypical murderers. In contrast to the prototype, fathers more often were present during childhood, but they usually provided negative role models. Also striking was the high incidence of deaths among parents, a rate almost five times higher than that observed in the prototype. The trauma of parental death can engender uncon-

Table 5–3
Percent of Cluster C Cases and Prototype Cases in Which Specific Long-Term Causal Factors Were Present

Long-Term Cause Category	*Cluster C (n = 13)*	*Prototype[a] (n = 20)*
Any negative role models	53.9	55.6
Father had criminal history	7.7	17.6
Father had substance abuse problems	30.8	11.8
Mother had criminal history	7.7	5.3
Mother had substance abuse problems	7.7	26.3
Sibling had criminal history	38.5	31.6
Sibling had substance abuse history	38.5	36.8
Any instability in childhood environment	69.2	72.2
One parent absent	53.8	68.4
Both parents absent	0.0	10.5
One or both parents died	23.1	5.3
One or more siblings died	0.3	0.0
Father was mentally ill	7.7	5.6
Mother was mentally ill	7.7	10.5
Sibling was mentally ill	7.7	5.3
Parents were divorced	46.2	63.2
Any lack of safety in childhood environment	69.2	73.7
Exposure to physical abuse	23.1	36.8
Exposure to sexual abuse	0.0	5.3
Exposure to pervasive neglect	69.2	63.2
Any disruption in childhood environment	30.8	52.6
Placement in institutional setting	23.1	47.4
Hospitalization in medical setting	7.7	10.5
Hospitalization in psychiatric setting	0.0	10.5

[a]Some missing data for three cases.

scious rage that may lie dormant for many years, only to emerge in response to some precipitating stress later in life.

The cluster C case examples provide a mixed picture of childhood behavior. A quantitative analysis of the childhood be-

Table 5–4
Percent of Cluster C Cases and Prototype Cases in Which Specific Childhood Behavior Abnormalities Were Present

Long-Term Cause Category	*Cluster C (n = 13)*	*Prototype[a] (n = 20)*
Any psychiatric symptoms	15.4	0.0
Speech disorders	0.0	0.0
Phobias	0.0	0.0
Sleep disturbances	15.4	0.0
Eating disturbances	15.4	0.0
Enuresis	0.0	0.0
Encopresis	0.0	0.0
Any disturbances of conduct	38.5	63.2
Fire setting	0.0	10.5
Cruelty to animals	0.0	15.8
Chronic lying	30.8	57.9
Repetitive stealing	38.5	47.4
Acts of vandalism	23.1	31.6
Any criminal behavior	38.5	45.0
Homicide	0.0	0.0
Rape	0.0	5.0
Other sexual crimes	0.0	10.0
Aggravated assault	7.7	25.0
Armed robbery	15.4	15.0
Other violent crimes	0.0	0.0
Property-related crimes	30.8	40.0
Drug-related crimes	7.7	5.0
Any school difficulties	69.2	70.0
Academic problems	61.5	70.0
Truancy problems	61.5	55.0
Any problems with relationships	92.3	94.7
School behavior problems	38.5	35.0
Violent behavior at school	15.4	20.0
Problems relating to father	84.6	84.2
Problems relating to mother	61.5	73.7
Problems relating to siblings	69.2	73.7
Difficulty making friends	38.5	68.4
Difficulty keeping friends	38.5	57.9
Repetitive temper outbursts	23.1	36.8
Chronic disobedience	46.2	57.9

[a]Some missing data for one case.

havior pattern of all thirteen cases in the cluster is presented in table 5–4. This analysis indicates that few cluster C murderers exhibited childhood psychiatric symptoms, in contrast to the almost universal presence of psychiatric distress in adult life. Few disturbances of conduct were observed relative to the prototype's experience, but prototypical murderers also were more behaviorally aberrant as adults. Fewer cluster C than prototypical murderers committed juvenile criminal offenses, and this finding predicts the relative infrequency of adult criminality in this cluster. Cluster C and the prototype have high rates of academic and truancy problems, as well as those relating to interpersonal relations. These high rates are not consonant with the relative occupational success of cluster C murderers but are consonant with their interpersonal difficulties experienced in adult life.

Psychoneurosis, Impoverished Self-esteem, and Stress in the Genesis of Homicidal Behavior

Let us now summarize the salient features that characterize cluster C. This cluster shares proximate causes such as impaired impulse control and interpersonal relations with the prototype. While somewhat less likely to espouse antisocial values, cluster C murderers suffer from an impoverished sense of self-esteem that is not seen in the prototype.

Cluster C murderers also exhibit both Axis I psychiatric disorders and Axis II personality disorders. The former disorders usually take the form of depression. The latter disorders include more low-impact disorders than are seen in the prototype. These low-impact disorders are marked by anxious, avoidant, or dependent behavior patterns.

Exposure to significant stresses just prior to or at the time of the crime were documented in all but one cluster C case. Moreover, these murderers blamed these stresses on their victims. Violence, however inappropriate or maladaptive, became a means to alleviate these stresses.

Cluster C murderers feel alienated and/or disenfranchised. Unlike their prototype counterparts, their substantive stakes in the community have been lost only recently. Moreover, the losses usually occur in proximity to the crime and are blamed on the victim. While prototypical murderers are angry at the world, cluster C murderers are angry at their victims or, as in the case of R.D., terrified by them.

Cluster C murderers may kill more than one victim, but they invariably do so in one explosive outburst. There is little, if any, deliberation before the act. In all but two cases, the assailant and victim(s) knew each other. With respect to motives, the desire for revenge and disputes over romance and money predominate. Such motives were found in nine of the thirteen cases (69 percent).

What special light can the cluster C profile shed on the dynamics of homicidal behavior? Cluster C adds several new elements to the paradigm described in chapter 3. While less antisocial in its basic orientation, cluster C demonstrates how exposure to stress, the impact of an impoverished sense of self-esteem, and the debilitating effects of psychoneuroses can produce a homicidal outcome. Psychoneuroses are influential because of how their associated anxiety states, compulsive behaviors, and depressive symptoms debilitate mental functions and promote self-defeating and self-destructive behaviors. These effects augment the maladaptive behavior patterns associated with personality disorders also common in this cluster. Stress disrupts or disables the person's coping mechanisms. Damage to self-esteem leaves individuals particularly sensitive to narcissistic assaults and likely to react in an extreme way to such assaults. Often cluster C murderers view their victims as having committed the assaults and, in the process, as having wrecked their lives. This in turn produces a powerful reason for targeting the victim for violent retaliatory action. In this sense, cluster C murderers commit more personal crimes than do prototypical or cluster B murderers, who tend to direct their violence more indiscriminately at a broader array of targets.

6
Substance Abuse, Personality Disorganization, and Homicide

The third variant of the prototype, cluster D, shares many of the prototype's proximate causal factors and introduces two additional factors—the effects of active substance abuse and intoxication—that have not yet played a prominent role in our discussions. Cluster D accounts for 15 percent of the total study population and together with clusters A, B, and C comprises more than two-thirds of the entire sample.

The Proximate Causal Pattern

Let us begin our discussion of cluster D with several illustrative case examples.

> E.S., thirty-two years of age and unmarried, encountered a man who allegedly had accosted and robbed his mother but had escaped prosecution. The other man taunted E.S. about having beaten the rap. When the man entered a local restaurant, E.S. returned home to retrieve a handgun he had bought for protection and then returned to the restaurant and killed the man.
>
> E.S. lived a lonely life devoid of relationships. He reported a series of injurious motorcycle accidents, which were the product of impulsive behavior. He also reported a history of explosive outbursts.
>
> E.S. acknowledged that he could not control his use of alcohol or other drugs. He began drinking to excess at

the age of thirteen, subsequently began using marijuana, and later became addicted to barbiturates and opiates. He also reported a ten-year history of PCP use, the last instance of which occurred approximately one week before his crime.

Just prior to the crime, E.S. consumed a large quantity of alcohol and moderate amounts of two tranquilizers, Valium and Transene. E.S. was arrested immediately after the crime, and a blood test for alcohol conducted two hours later measured a level well within the intoxicated range (0.20 mg percent).

E.S. described a long history of phobic symptoms and anxiety for which doctors prescribed a variety of antianxiety medications. Based on his history of impulsivity, temperamental outbursts, self-destructive behavior, frequent mood swings, and chronic feelings of emptiness, E.S. easily met the criteria for a diagnosis of borderline personality disorder.

While active substance abuse, intoxication, and personality dysfunction were the predominant proximate causal factors in this case, other factors contributed as well. E.S. had a history of other instances of antisocial behavior. His lack of skills, assets, or prospects engendered feelings of alienation and disenfranchisement. He also experienced ongoing stresses in his life, including chronic health problems and unresolved feelings about his father's death, which had occurred several years before the crime.

K.R., a twenty-two–year–old unmarried drifter, was passing through a rural community with a companion when he met two locals and began drinking with them. Within the next several hours, a conflict erupted between the men, and K.R. stabbed and robbed his newfound drinking buddies.

K.R. had been living the life of a drifter for some years and had no close interpersonal attachments. He acknowledged temper outbursts and inadequate restraint in relation to drug and alcohol use, which were corroborated by others. These findings substantiated a clear-cut lack of impulse control.

K.R.'s drug and alcohol abuse problems began in the ninth grade with weekend beer binges. Before long, these binges evolved into daily alcohol abuse. Shortly thereafter, marijuana abuse began, as did the use of Quaaludes, a hypnotic sedative. Over the years, K.R. said he experimented with amphetamines but denied using other illicit drugs.

Eyewitness accounts and evidence found at the crime scene indicated that K.R. had been drinking heavily on the day of the crime. A blood test for alcohol conducted four hours after the crime measured a level below the intoxicated range, but by extrapolation the level was calculated as having been within the intoxicated range at the time of the crime.

In addition to symptomatology indicative of a polysubstance dependence disorder, K.R. described symptoms of anxiety and despondency. His history also was consistent with a diagnosis of borderline personality disorder. Although K.R. initially denied responsibility for his crime, he later changed his story and claimed self-defense despite considerable evidence suggesting that the primary motive for his crime was robbery. It is probable that the homicides resulted from resistance on the part of his victims, who also were intoxicated.

Additional contributory proximate causes included K.R.'s prior antisocial history of petty criminality and his alienated and disenfranchised status.

D.J., a thirty-two–year–old divorced bus driver, was helping his mother dispose of a deceased aunt's belongings in a community seventy miles from his home. One evening he "scored some crack cocaine" and after using it experienced hallucinations and increasingly severe paranoid ideation. The paranoia precipitated an episode of violence during which D.J. bludgeoned his mother to death with a board. Later, as the effects of the cocaine dissipated, D.J. realized what he had done and called for assistance.

Since no tests to ascertain the presence of cocaine were conducted, D.J.'s state of intoxication can only be estimated from his delusional and hallucinatory status at the time of his arrest several hours after the homicidal event. Neither the authorities nor D.J. could establish any rational motive for the crime, which appears to have been purely substance induced.

D.J. was living alone at the time of his crime, but he had been involved several years before in a short-lived and highly volatile marital relationship. D.J. acknowledged impulse control problems when he was intoxicated. He minimized his dependence on cocaine and alcohol despite much evidence to the contrary.

D.J.'s history of prior antisocial behavior was limited to several outbursts of domestic violence while he was married and for which he was sent to a diversion program. Stress may have played a role in his mother's murder, as he was between jobs and was feeling economically insecure at the time.

D.O., a twenty-five–year–old married male, spent most of one afternoon drinking and snorting cocaine with his wife. The couple then attended a party at which they continued to use alcohol and cocaine. Leaving the party in the throws of a heated argument about his wife's allegedly flirtatious behavior with other men, they went home and continued to quarrel. The quarrel became more heated, and D.O. shot his wife with a shotgun that was kept in the home. She later died in a hospital.

D.O. described a number of prior marriages and relationships, all of which were volatile, unstable, and at times violent. He acknowledged that his explosive outbursts were always associated with intoxication. He clearly met the criteria for the diagnosis of a mixed substance abuse disorder involving alcohol, marijuana, and cocaine. Substance abuse had begun during adolescence and persisted thereafter.

The precipitant in this case was a marital quarrel that reflected D.O.'s jealous rage. Whether the wife actually

> flirted with other men at the party could not be ascertained, and his perception of this may have been the result of drug-induced paranoia. D.O. acknowledged that he was very angry with his wife at the time of the crime but denied that he harbored any murderous intent toward her.

The pattern illustrated by these cases suggests that substance abuse and intoxication are prominent causal factors in this cluster but that social isolation, marked impulsivity, and personality dysfunction that is at times severe enough to warrant a personality disorder diagnosis also are relevant factors. Such a conclusion is supported by the quantitative analysis of all cluster D cases (table 6–1). The data in this table clearly demonstrate a pattern of baseline personality dysfunctions consonant with those in the prototype. The incidence of personality disorders was almost as high in cluster D as in the prototype, but the pattern was very different. In cluster D murderers, antisocial personality disorders were almost unknown, and almost half of the cases manifested low-impact disorders or no disorder at all.

Rationalizing motives were even more prominent in cluster D than in the prototype, but such motives were more personalized, much like those observed in cluster C. Romantic conflicts played a role in five cases and revenge in three others. There was a scattering of other motives. In contrast to the prototype, only one cluster D murderer denied responsibility for his crime.

Several other differences between cluster D and the prototype were noted. Substance abuse was universal in cluster D, with a discernible preference for alcohol over other substances. Alcohol abuse was a factor in almost 87 percent of the cases and other substance abuse in only 53 percent. Intoxication was universally present in cluster D, but it was almost unknown in the prototype.

Based on these findings, cluster D cases share the following proximate causal pattern with the prototype:

1. Most exhibited impairments of interpersonal relations and impulse control.

Table 6–1
Percent of Cluster D Cases and Prototype Cases in Which Specific Proximate Causal Factors Were Present

Proximate Cause Category	*Cluster D (n = 15)*	*Prototype (n = 20)*
Baseline mental functions		
Impaired interpersonal relations	80.0	95.0
Impaired impulse control	60.0	85.0
Impaired reality testing	13.3	0.0
Impaired thinking	13.3	5.0
Impaired cognition	0.0	5.0
Impaired self-image	40.0	5.0
Antisocial values	73.3	75.0
Alienation/disenfranchisement	73.3	75.0
Presence of Axis I symptomatic psychiatric disorders		
Psychoses	0.0	0.0
Psychoneuroses	0.0	5.0
Substance abuse disorders	100.0	0.0
Behavior/organic/mental retardation	0.0	25.0
No Axis I disorder	0.0	70.0
Presence of Axis II personality disorders		
Antisocial personality	6.7	50.0
Borderline, paranoid, schizoid, or schizotypal personality	46.7	35.0
Histrionic or narcissistic personality	0.0	5.0
Low-impact disorders (avoidant, dependent, obsessive-compulsive, or passive-aggressive)	26.7	0.0
No Axis II disorder	20.0	10.0
Presence of substance abuse problems (with or without diagnosis of substance abuse disorder)		
Alcohol abuse only	46.7	5.0
Drug abuse only	13.3	5.0
Both alcohol and drug abuse	40.0	10.0
Presence of transient factors		
Rationalizing or justifying motives	86.7	70.0
Intoxication	100.0	5.0
Significant stress	60.0	40.0

2. Most met the criteria for the diagnosis of an Axis II personality disorder, but the pattern of such disorders differed from that seen in the prototype.

3. Almost all offered some rationalizing motive for their crime, although these motives differed somewhat from those of the prototype.

4. In many cases, a failure of socialization and the presence of antisocial values were noted.
5. Many cluster D murderers expressed feelings of alienation and/or disenfranchisement.

Cluster D cases differ from the prototype in the following ways:

1. All exhibited active substance abuse problems and met the criteria for the diagnosis of an Axis I substance abuse disorder.
2. All were intoxicated at the time of their crimes.
3. Exposure to significant stress was present in more than half of the cases.

The Demographic Pattern

Cluster D's demographic pattern, presented in table 6–2, is no surprise. In most respects, cluster D's pattern is similar to that of

Table 6–2
Percent of Cluster D Cases and Prototype Cases in Which Specific Demographic Characteristics Were Present

Demographic Category	*Cluster D (n = 15)*	*Prototype (n = 20)*
Assailant is male	100.0	90.0
Assailant is female	0.0	10.0
Assailant has prior criminal convictions	66.7	65.0
Assailant has no prior criminal convictions	33.3	35.0
Victim is known to assailant	66.7	70.0
Victim is not known to assailant	33.3	30.0
Assailant committed homicide only	86.7	65.0
Assailant committed homicide and rape	0.0	25.0
Assailant committed homicide and robbery	13.3	10.0
Assailant is younger than 18 years old	0.0	5.0
Assailant is 18 to 24 years old	33.3	25.0
Assailant is 25 to 39 years old	60.0	50.0
Assailant is 40 years or older	6.7	20.0
Assailant killed only one victim	73.3	70.0
Assailant killed more than one victim	26.7	30.0

the prototype. Among the findings that do differ are the absence of women assailants and the confinement of all but one case to the age range eighteen to thirty-nine years. Neither of these observations is particularly surprising, given the propensity of substance abusers to be young adult males.

The Long-Term Causal and Childhood Behavior Patterns

To examine patterns of long-term causality and childhood behavior in cluster D, additional historical information must be added to the illustrative case examples.

> E.S. came from an intact home, but his father was a chronic and severe alcoholic, a condition that required frequent hospitalization. His father died a violent death at the hands of another alcoholic patient while hospitalized in a detoxification facility. No abuse or neglect was reported in the family, which was held together by the mother. Perhaps this accounts in part for the ferocity with which E.S. reacted to his mother's assailant. E.S. did experience one prolonged hospitalization as a child for a serious infectious illness.
>
> E.S.'s childhood included a history of extreme fears that evolved into adult phobic symptoms. No evidence of conduct disturbances or juvenile criminality was noted. E.S. experienced academic, behavior, and truancy problems in school and did not complete the eleventh grade. He was a loner who did not make or keep friends easily, and his relationships at home, except that with his mother, were equally dysfunctional.

> Like E.S., K.R. suffered serious losses and disruptions during childhood, and he also was abused. His father was killed in Vietnam when K.R. was eight or nine years of age. His mother remarried an alcoholic who physically abused K.R. She divorced this man when K.R. was about fourteen years of age. Shortly thereafter, she left K.R. and

his siblings in the care of friends for several months, causing the children confusion and apprehension. After she returned, K.R. lived with her until age seventeen, when he left home to pursue a nomadic existence. K.R. was hospitalized several times during childhood for surgical procedures.

K.R. demonstrated a more consistent pattern of behavioral aberrations during childhood than did E.S. Like E.S., he engaged in drug-related activity in adolescence, but he also engaged in repetitive stealing. His school performance was disrupted by a learning disability and by chronic truancy problems, and he failed to complete the eleventh grade. Like E.S., K.R. was described as an isolated and troubled youngster who kept to himself.

D.J. grew up in a more stable childhood environment but one in which no male role model was present. D.J.'s parents divorced when he was an infant, and he had no further contact with his father. No abuse or disruptions occurred during his childhood.

D.J. was described as an isolated child who neither made nor kept friends. He exhibited no other obvious childhood disturbances. He did not manifest psychiatric symptoms or conduct disturbances, and he had no juvenile criminal history. He completed high school with no academic or truancy difficulties.

D.O. experienced the most deprived childhood existence of these case examples. He was raised by a succession of relatives and was at times placed in foster homes because both of his parents were involved in substance abuse–related criminal activity and were incarcerated for long periods. As a consequence, D.O. suffered profound neglect. He also was a victim of physical abuse in at least one of the foster homes to which he was sent.

D.O. represents something of an enigma in part because relatively little information is available about his childhood. D.O. could not recall psychiatric symptomatology, but it is almost inconceivable that he would not have been depressed, given the pervasive neglect to which he was exposed. Surprisingly, no conduct disturbances or instances of juvenile criminality were reported. D.O. exhibited both academic and truancy problems and did not graduate from high school, but he later obtained a general equivalency diploma (GED). Like the others, D.O. was an isolated child who kept very much to himself.

These illustrative cases suggest a substantial pattern of childhood trauma. Particularly striking are the absence of positive male role models, and the presence of negative role models, especially concerning the substance-dependent behavior of one or both parents. Themes of abandonment and loss predominate.

Table 6–3
Percent of Cluster D Cases and Prototype Cases in Which Specific Long-Term Causal Factors Were Present

Long-Term Cause Category	*Cluster D*[a] *(n = 15)*	*Prototype*[a] *(n = 20)*
Any negative role models	75.0	55.6
Father had criminal history	16.7	17.6
Father had substance abuse problems	50.0	11.8
Mother had criminal history	6.7	5.3
Mother had substance abuse problems	13.3	26.3
Sibling had criminal history	33.3	31.6
Sibling had substance abuse problems	20.0	36.8
Any instability in childhood environment	66.7	72.2
One parent absent	46.7	68.4
both parents absent	26.7	10.5
One or Both parents died	6.7	5.3
One or more siblings died	6.7	0.0
Father was mentally ill	0.0	5.6
Mother was mentally ill	0.0	10.5
Sibling was mentally ill	0.0	5.3
Parents were divorced	53.3	63.2
Any lack of safety in childhood environment	46.7	73.7
Exposure to physical abuse	26.7	36.8
Exposure to sexual abuse	0.0	5.3
Exposure to pervasive neglect	46.7	63.2
Any disruption in childhood environment	46.7	52.6
Placement in institutional setting	33.3	47.4
Hospitalization in medical setting	6.7	10.5
Hospitalization in psychiatric setting	6.7	10.5

[a]Some missing data for three cases.

A quantitative analysis of the trauma pattern of all cluster D cases is presented in table 6–3. Overall, marginally lower levels of trauma relative to those noted in the prototype are apparent.

Table 6–4
Percent of Cluster D Cases and Prototype Cases in Which Specific Childhood Behavior Abnormalities Were Present

Behavior Category	*Cluster D (n = 15)*	*Prototype[a] (n = 20)*
Any psychiatric symptoms	13.3	0.0
Speech disorders	0.0	0.0
Phobias	13.3	0.0
Sleep disturbances	0.0	0.0
Eating disturbances	0.0	0.0
Enuresis	0.0	0.0
Encopresis	0.0	0.0
Any disturbances of conduct	46.7	63.2
Fire setting	0.0	10.5
Cruelty to animals	0.0	15.8
Chronic lying	33.3	57.9
Repetitive stealing	26.7	47.4
Acts of vandalism	6.7	31.6
Any criminal behavior	33.3	45.0
Homicide	0.0	0.0
Rape	0.0	5.0
Other sexual crimes	0.0	10.0
Aggravated assault	6.7	25.0
Armed robbery	6.7	15.0
Other violent crimes	0.0	0.0
Property-related crimes	26.7	40.0
Drug-related crimes	20.0	5.0
Any school difficulties	80.0	70.0
Academic problems	80.0	70.0
Truancy problems	66.7	55.0
Any problems with relationships	86.7	94.7
School behavior problems	53.3	35.0
Violent behavior at school	6.7	20.0
Problems relating to father	80.0	84.2
Problems relating to mother	53.3	73.7
Problems relating to siblings	53.3	73.7
Difficulty making friends	53.3	68.4
Difficulty keeping friends	53.3	57.9
Repetitive temper outbursts	26.7	36.8
Chronic disobedience	33.3	57.9

[a]Some missing data for one case.

Striking among the findings is the high incidence of substance abuse problems among the fathers of cluster D murderers, a rate more than four times higher than that found in the prototype. Given the substance abuse problems noted in cluster D murderers, this finding suggests a link between the murderers' behavior and that of a powerful negative role model.

Almost as striking is the finding of a high incidence of absence from the home of both parents, an event experienced by more than one-quarter of all cluster D murderers. This incidence rate is two and a half times higher than that found in the prototype. It should be noted that although disruptions in the childhood environment were common in the case examples, they were not characteristic of the cluster as a whole, occurring in less than half of the cases. This incidence rate is lower than that of the prototype.

With respect to childhood behavior, difficulties at school and problems establishing interpersonal relations were prominent in the case examples. The quantitative analysis presented in table 6–4 shows that most cluster D cases had these difficulties.

Cluster D murderers manifested less antisocial behavior during childhood than their prototype counterparts. Since the incidence of adult criminal behavior was high in both clusters, cluster D murderers appear to have begun their antisocial behavior later in life, in all probability in connection with substance abuse.

Adding the Impact of Substance Abuse to Personality Dysfunction

Let us now summarize the salient features that characterize cluster D. Some of the impairments that characterize the prototype are evident in this cluster. Isolation and detachment from others cripple interpersonal relations. Frequent temperamental outbursts and the lack of control over drug use indicate poor impulse control. Behavior indicative of antisocial attitudes is common. Also, cluster D murderers have feelings of alienation and perceive themselves to be disenfranchised. Such feelings and perceptions may be long-standing or of recent vintage. Some cluster D murderers have a modicum of success in adult life, only to experience its loss, usually as a consequence of substance abuse. Rationalizing motives are common. In eleven of the fifteen cluster D cases, a specific motivational link between the assailant and the victim could be discerned, most often a romantic conflict or a quest for revenge.

Cluster D murderers generally manifest the symptoms of some type of personality disorder, but the pattern of such disorders differs from that which the prototype manifests. More borderline and low-impact disorders are diagnosed, and antisocial personality disorders are very rare. Finally, cluster D murderers have been exposed to significant stress, as noted in 60 percent of the cases, an occurrence that is somewhat less common in the prototype.

The dual impact of active substance abuse and intoxication, the hallmark of cluster D proximate causality, must be added to the above core. Both of these factors were found in every case in this cluster. Active substance abuse contributes a preoccupation with substance acquisition and leads to the neglect of other important life tasks. In addition, substance abuse has debilitating effects on all baseline mental functions. These effects may be subtle or pervasive and dramatic. Intoxication causes confusion, disorientation, impairment of judgment, and a diminution of inhibitions that may act to discourage ill-advised behaviors. Since inhibiting factors are already marginal in the cluster D murderers, the effects of intoxication are even more profound than they might otherwise be.

What is the dynamic mechanism at work in this cluster? The debilitation inflicted on mental functioning by alcohol and other psychoactive substances must be added to the paradigm presented in chapter 3, which emphasizes devalued targets, poor impulse control, antisocial orientation, and the presence of rationalizing motives. Very striking in these cases is a sense that few if any of these murderers would have committed homicidal acts if they had been sober. While they did express motives, the cluster D murderers also usually expressed regrets and said that had they been less intoxicated and more in command of their behavior, they would not have committed the homicidal act. This can be interpreted as a self-serving rationalization, but as we will see in the next chapter, not all intoxicated murderers express this view.

7
Substance Abuse, Antisocial Personality Disorders, and Homicide

Some of the most dangerous murderers in the study sample can be found in the fourth and final variant of the prototype, cluster E. Active substance abuse and intoxication at the time of the crime are prominent proximate causal factors in this cluster, as they are in cluster D. Cluster E also is marked by exceedingly antisocial and predatory behavior. This cluster represents 18 percent of the total study population and together with the prototype and its other variants accounts for 86 percent of the entire study sample.

The Proximate Causal Pattern

Let us begin our discussion of cluster E with the introduction of some illustrative case examples.

> J.M., twenty-five years old and married, was selling novelties door-to-door when he encountered the rental agent for an apartment complex. He could not prevail upon her to buy anything but announced an intention to return later in the day in the role of a prospective tenant. His real intention was robbery, but finding her alone, he bound the woman and was preparing to sexually assault her when he slit her throat instead.
>
> Initially, J.M. denied responsibility for the crime, but

once he concluded that the evidence against him was compelling, he ceased his denial and became quite matter-of-fact about it. He noted that he needed money to buy drugs and needed to kill his victim to prevent being identified by her. He continued to deny any sexual intent, however. Considerable evidence indicated that J.M. also committed a series of combined robberies and sexual assaults in a three-week period prior to this crime. He expressed no remorse in relation to any of his criminal activities and no concern about his victims. After learning that the homicide victim was a terminal cancer patient, he remarked that she would have "died soon anyway."

J.M. was married at the time of his crime, but his wife dropped out of sight shortly after his arrest and could not be interviewed. He had led an antisocial and predatory life-style since adolescence. He stole from and cheated virtually everyone with whom he came into contact. This included both victims and criminal associates. J.M. acknowledged extreme discomfort around people except when high on cocaine. Dependence on cocaine began during adolescence and persisted thereafter. J.M. admitted that he generally gratified his impulses of the moment without reference to consequences.

Like all other cluster E murderers, J.M. easily met the criteria for a diagnosis of antisocial personality disorder, given his history of school difficulties, delinquency, continual misbehavior during adolescence, and inability to sustain consistent work behavior or otherwise act responsibly as an adult. J.M.'s history of criminal activity included convictions for assault, burglary, rape, robbery, and possession for sale of illicit drugs. He had served several prison sentences. He expressed marked feelings of alienation toward everyone and everything, and his behavior toward virtually everyone can be described as predatory and exploitive.

On the day of his crime, J.M. snorted cocaine every few hours, as had been his practice during the preceding three weeks.

J.T., thirty-one years old and divorced, was "riding the rails" when he encountered another drifter. J.T. initially maintained that the other man attempted to rob him and that he defended himself, but ultimately he acknowledged that he had robbed and then stabbed his victim. Since J.T. had forced the victim to remove all of his clothing, a second motive in this case may have been homosexual rape, a possibility that J.T. assiduously denied. Despite his initial denial to me, J.T. had bragged about the crime to the police when he was apprehended.

J.T. was described by family members as a loner. He was married only once and even then lived with his wife for only fourteen days. He could recall only one other heterosexual relationship and described it as highly volatile and unstable. J.T., a self-proclaimed "predator," acknowledged that he viewed the world as a jungle in which people "either take or are taken." He admitted sudden outbursts of anger when thwarted, often in association with drug abuse. J.T.'s history was replete with multiple inpatient and outpatient treatments for alcohol and drug abuse. Each episode was associated with psychotic symptoms, including auditory and visual hallucinations and paranoid ideation. There was no history of such symptoms at any other time. J.T.'s polysubstance abuse included alcohol, LSD, amphetamines, marijuana, and Valium.

Prior to the homicide, J.T. was known to the criminal justice system but was viewed as a petty offender. In addition to multiple instances of petty criminality, his antisocial orientation was evidenced by the complete neglect of a child he had fathered.

A drifter, J.T. could be described as alienated and disenfranchised. He never possessed any resources, skills, or assets. He maintained that he was drinking heavily at the time of his crime, but because he was not apprehended until several days later, there was no way to corroborate his level of intoxication. It is known that J.T.'s victim was highly intoxicated at the time of his death, and it is at least possible that the two men were drinking together.

D.E., thirty-two years old and unmarried, was interrupted by a woman who returned to her home while he was burglarizing it. D.E. shot and killed the woman either because she attempted to call for help or to eliminate the only witness to his crime. D.E. continued to deny responsibility for the crime despite conclusive physical evidence linking him to it.

D.E. had no friends and had never maintained an intimate relationship. He was a professional burglar who stole to support his need for illicit substances. He spent more time in institutions than out of them, and he invariably projected blame for his criminality onto others who he said had cheated him. He expressed the beliefs that "people will screw me if they can" and "I am going to do it to them before they can do it to me." His life was characterized by impulsive outbursts of anger generally directed at employers for whom he worked sporadically. Such behavior often precipitated dismissals, which led in turn to additional criminal behavior. D.E.'s antisocial lifestyle included the sale of illicit drugs.

D.E. had abused alcohol and amphetamines continuously since adolescence. He described visual hallucinations and paranoid ideation in association with substance abuse but not at other times. Proof of intoxication at the time of the crime was unavailable, but D.E.'s documented continuous use of both alcohol and amphetamines suggests that intoxication was likely. He described chronic depressive symptomatology, and he easily met the criteria for a diagnosis of antisocial personality disorder.

D.B., twenty-eight years of age and unmarried, found himself without transportation when his own automobile malfunctioned. He abducted a young woman outside a convenience store ostensibly solely to steal her car. However, some evidence suggests that the woman was sexually assaulted, although D.B. was never charged with this crime. Ultimately, D.B. shot and killed his victim and disposed of her body in a dumpster. He denied all responsibility for the crime, blaming it on a mysterious hitchhiker whom he insisted he had picked up after the abduction. The existence of this man could never be corroborated.

D.B.'s criminal behavior was testament to his antisocial orientation. He had been convicted of armed robbery and of the sale of illicit drugs and had served several prison terms. D.B. also had a long history of substance abuse, including dependence on marijuana, heroin, amphetamines, and cocaine. He reported paranoid ideation and hallucinatory experiences in relation to drug use but not at any other time. D.B. estimated that his drug dependence was costing him $200 per day at the time of his arrest and said that he had used amphetamines and cocaine on the day of the crime. D.B.'s crime appears to have been the product of his need to support his drug habit but also suggests predatory behavior to fulfill sexual needs. The homicide was in all probability an attempt to eliminate the sole witness to the crime. D.B. expressed no remorse in connection with the crime.

These case histories reveal that cluster E murderers are predatory, dangerous, and malevolent. Clearly they view their victims as objects to be exploited at their whim. They are antisocial, lack any remorse, and exhibit few if any inhibitions. To the extent that they are present at all, inhibitions are disarmed by the effects of substance abuse and/or intoxication.

This portrait is corroborated by the quantitative analysis of all cluster E cases presented in table 7–1. This analysis reveals that impairment of interpersonal relations and impulse control was even more common in this cluster than in cluster D and as common as in the prototype. Additionally, an antisocial orientation and a sense of alienation and/or disenfranchisement were more common than in cluster D or the prototype.

All cluster E cases exhibited substance abuse problems, and in all but two cases, the primary Axis I diagnosis was that of substance abuse disorder. Drug abuse predominated, affecting more than 83 percent of these murderers. Alcohol abuse was present in 61 percent of the cases. This is in contrast to cluster D, where alcohol abuse predominated. The most commonly

Table 7–1
Percent of Cluster E Cases and Prototype Cases in Which Specific Proximate Causal Factors Were Present

Proximate Cause Category	*Cluster E (n = 18)*	*Prototype (n = 20)*
Baseline mental functions		
Impaired interpersonal relations	100.0	95.0
Impaired impulse control	83.3	85.0
Impaired reality testing	5.6	0.0
Impaired thinking	11.1	5.0
Impaired cognition	16.7	5.0
Impaired self-image	0.0	5.0
Antisocial values	88.9	75.0
Alienation/disenfranchisement	77.8	75.0
Presence of Axis I symptomatic psychiatric disorders		
Psychoses	0.0	0.0
Psychoneuroses	5.6	5.0
Substance abuse disorders	88.8	0.0
Behavior/organic/mental retardation	5.6	25.0
No Axis I disorder	0.0	70.0
Presence of Axis II personality disorders		
Antisocial personality	100.0	50.0
Borderline, paranoid, schizoid, or schizotypal personality	0.0	35.0
Histrionic or narcissistic personality	0.0	5.0
Low-impact disorders (avoidant, dependent, obsessive-compulsive, or passive-aggressive)	0.0	0.0
No Axis II disorder	0.0	10.0
Presence of substance abuse problems (with or without diagnosis of substance abuse disorder)		
Alcohol abuse only	16.7	5.0
Drug abuse only	38.9	5.0
Both alcohol and drug abuse	44.4	10.0
Presence of transient factors		
Rationalizing or justifying motives	44.4	70.0
Intoxication	77.8	5.0
Significant stress	22.2	40.0

abused drugs in this cluster were cocaine, amphetamines, and heroin. While intoxication was very common in cluster E, it could not be documented in all cases.

All cluster E murderers easily met the criteria for an Axis II diagnosis of antisocial personality disorder. This is twice the incidence rate observed in the prototype and also contrasts with the findings in cluster D, where borderline and low-impact disorders predominated.

Almost 45 percent of all cluster E murderers denied responsibility for their crimes, accounting for a low incidence rate for rationalizing motives. Such denials were more common than in the prototype (30 percent) and much more common than those in cluster D (10 percent). Twenty-eight percent of these homicides were committed to eliminate a witness to another violent crime (robbery or rape), bringing the combined total of denials and detection-avoidance motives to almost 75 percent, a pattern unmatched in any other cluster.

Based on these findings, cluster E murderers share the following proximate causal pattern with the prototype:

1. All exhibited impairment of interpersonal relations, and most exhibited impairment of impulse control.
2. In all cases, a failure of socialization and the presence of antisocial values were noted.
3. Most expressed feelings of alienation and/or disenfranchisement.
4. All met the criteria for the diagnosis of an Axis II personality disorder, but the pattern of these disorders differed from that of the prototype in that all suffered from antisocial personality disorders.

The following proximate causal pattern found in cluster E murderers differs from that of the prototype:

1. All exhibited active substance abuse problems, and almost all manifested a primary Axis I diagnosis of substance abuse disorder.
2. Many were intoxicated at the time of their crimes.
3. Less than half offered any rationalizing motive for their crimes.

The Demographic Pattern

The demographic pattern presented in table 7–2 reflects this cluster's pervasive antisocial character. The analysis reveals that

Table 7–2
Percent of Cluster E Cases and Prototype Cases in Which Specific Demographic Characteristics Were Present

Demographic Category	*Cluster E (n = 18)*	*Prototype (n = 20)*
Assailant is male	94.4	90.0
Assailant is female	5.6	10.0
Assailant has prior criminal convictions	88.9	65.0
Assailant has no prior criminal convictions	11.1	35.0
Victim is known to assailant	27.8	70.0
Victim is not known to assailant	72.2	30.0
Assailant committed homicide only	33.3	65.0
Assailant committed homicide and rape	27.8	25.0
Assailant committed homicide and robbery	38.9	10.0
Assailant is younger than 18 years old	0.0	5.0
Assailant is 18 to 24 years old	44.4	25.0
Assailant is 25 to 39 years old	50.0	50.0
Assailant is 40 years or older	5.6	20.0
Assailant killed only one victim	83.3	70.0
Assailant killed more than one victim	16.7	30.0

only one of the eighteen cluster E murderers was a woman. Also, the incidence of prior criminal convictions was higher in this cluster than in any other, underscoring its antisocial nature. Almost 75 percent of cluster E assailants killed strangers, a finding that exceeds by far the rate for any other cluster. Two-thirds of all cluster E murderers committed complex crimes, either homicide and rape or homicide and robbery; this incidence rate is much higher than that observed in any other cluster.

Cluster E murderers are almost always males between the ages of eighteen and thirty-nine who usually are already known to the criminal justice system and who commit complex crimes against strangers. This is a unique profile when compared to the other clusters, and it reflects the extreme antisocial and predatory nature of these individuals.

The Long-Term Causal and Childhood Behavior Patterns

To examine the pattern of long-term causality and childhood behavior in cluster E murderers, it is necessary to add to the illustrative case examples already presented.

J.M. came from a poor, uneducated Appalachian family. Both parents were alcoholics, as were several older siblings. The siblings abused illicit drugs as well. The family was intact but highly dysfunctional in terms of interpersonal relationships. Any semblance of closeness or mutual support was lacking. J.M. was repeatedly abused physically by his older brothers and their friends. He also was sexually abused at least twice.

J.M. was a bed wetter until age fifteen and suffered from frequent terrifying nightmares throughout his childhood. His childhood behavior included substance abuse, chronic lying, persistent misbehavior, frequent vandalism, and stealing. By the age of seventeen, he had committed substance-related criminal offenses and a succession of burglaries and had been incarcerated several times. He demonstrated no capacity for intimate relationships and had trouble making and keeping friends. He also was a behavior problem at school.

J.T.'s family background was the most stable of any of the case examples. He grew up in a career military family in which changes of residence occurred frequently. J.T.'s father frequently was absent from the family home for prolonged periods, and when he was there, he abused alcohol. The mother was described as a more stable force within the family. J.T. was one of four siblings, and he and one brother were described as the black sheep of the family because of their involvement with both substance abuse and antisocial activity. The other two siblings appear to have fared better and have led stable, law-abiding lives.

J.T. was an alcoholic adolescent and exhibited chronic disobedient behavior during childhood and adolescence. He did not, however, have a record of juvenile criminal offenses. J.T. did graduate from high school, but he was categorized as an underachiever by his teachers. By his own admission, J.T. preferred to drink beer, chase girls, and be truant rather than pursue what could have been a more successful academic career.

D.E. came from a totally chaotic family setting in which

both parents abused illicit drugs and in which all eleven children were forced to fend for themselves. This family was so dysfunctional that D.E. was removed from his parents' custody at the age of five and placed in a succession of foster homes. He was physically abused in at least one foster home. He was adopted at the age of seven but could not adjust to his new family's behavioral or academic expectations. Ultimately, his behavior became unmanageable, and he was placed in a succession of juvenile detention facilities and state hospitals.

D.E. probably was depressed during childhood, given the extreme pattern of neglect and abuse to which he was exposed, but definitive evidence of this was not found in his records. A documented history of pervasive lying, stealing, vandalism, and runaway behavior was recorded. By the end of adolescence, he had been convicted of aggravated assault, the sale of illicit drugs, auto theft, and multiple burglaries. His school performance was inadequate, with evidence of chronic academic difficulties and almost constant truancy problems. His records were replete with behavior problems in school, including several violent incidents.

D.B. described his mother as a saint and his father as a monster. His father, who was both alcoholic and mentally ill, abused family members physically and emotionally until his mother left him when D.B. was nine years of age. His mother provided some stability in D.B.'s childhood, but it was clearly too little and too late. Both D.B. and a younger sister were plagued by substance abuse problems, which included marijuana and cocaine abuse.

D.B.'s conduct disturbances began in childhood and included chronic lying and stealing. He had a juvenile criminal record that include vandalism and theft. Other antisocial behavior that had gone undetected was reported during the evaluation. Chronic academic problems did not prevent D.B. from graduating from high school, however, and he reported some success in high school athletic programs.

All of the case examples include a pattern of parental substance abuse. Physical and sexual abuse, while not universal, frequently occurred. Disruptions of the childhood environment also were evident because of frequent moves or juvenile incarcerations. Additionally, these murderers experienced a lack of constancy and safety in childhood.

This pattern of abuse and neglect is corroborated by the analysis of all eighteen cases in the cluster (table 7–3). It reveals that in more than half the cases, the father was afflicted by a substance abuse problem, a rate achieved only in cluster D.

Cluster E murderers were exposed to physical and sexual

Table 7–3
Percent of Cluster E Cases and Prototype Cases in Which Specific Long-Term Causal Factors Were Present

Long-Term Cause Category	*Cluster E*[a] *(n = 18)*	*Prototype*[b] *(n = 20)*
Any negative role models	70.6	55.6
Father had criminal history	0.0	17.6
Father had substance abuse problems	52.9	11.8
Mother had criminal history	0.0	5.3
Mother had substance abuse problems	33.3	26.3
Sibling had criminal history	38.9	31.6
Sibling had substance abuse problems	50.0	36.8
Any instability in childhood environment	58.8	72.2
One parent absent	27.8	68.4
Both parents absent	11.1	10.5
One or both parents died	22.2	5.3
One or more siblings died	0.0	0.0
Father was mentally ill	5.9	5.6
Mother was mentally ill	16.7	10.5
Sibling was mentally ill	11.1	5.3
Parents were divorced	22.2	63.2
Any lack of safety in childhood environment	66.7	73.7
Exposure to physical abuse	38.9	36.8
Exposure to sexual abuse	16.7	5.3
Exposure to pervasive neglect	55.6	63.2
Any disruption in childhood environment	50.0	52.6
Placement in institutional setting	44.4	47.4
Hospitalization in medical setting	11.1	10.5
Hospitalization in psychiatric setting	11.1	10.5

[a]Some missing data for one case.
[b]Some missing data for three cases.

abuse and to pervasive neglect at rates comparable to those observed in the prototype but higher than those observed in the other clusters. This observation may be an important clue in

Table 7–4

Percent of Cluster E Cases and Prototype Cases in Which Specific Childhood Behavior Abnormalities Were Present

Behavior Cause Category	*Cluster E*[a] *(n = 18)*	*Prototype*[a] *(n = 20)*
Any psychiatric symptoms	5.6	0.0
Speech disorders	0.0	0.0
Phobias	0.0	0.0
Sleep disturbances	5.6	0.0
Eating disturbances	0.0	0.0
Enuresis	5.6	0.0
Encopresis	0.0	0.0
Any disturbances of conduct	83.3	63.2
Fire setting	5.6	10.5
Cruelty to animals	5.9	15.8
Chronic lying	83.3	57.9
Repetitive stealing	72.2	47.4
Acts of vandalism	38.9	31.6
Any criminal behavior	66.7	45.0
Homicide	0.0	0.0
Rape	11.1	5.0
Other sexual crimes	11.1	10.0
Aggravated assault	16.7	25.0
Armed robbery	0.0	15.0
Other violent crimes	11.1	0.0
Property-related crimes	55.6	40.0
Drug-related crimes	44.4	5.0
Any school difficulties	100.0	70.0
Academic problems	83.3	70.0
Truancy problems	94.4	55.0
Any problems with relationships	100.0	94.7
School behavior problems	61.1	35.0
Violent behavior at school	5.6	20.0
Problems relating to father	77.8	84.2
Problems relating to mother	55.6	73.7
Problems relating to siblings	50.0	73.7
Difficulty making friends	50.0	68.4
Difficulty keeping friends	55.6	57.9
Repetitive temper outbursts	55.6	36.8
Chronic disobedience	83.3	57.9

[a]Some missing data for one case.

ascertaining why the murderers in the prototype and in cluster E were more predatory and antisocial than those in the other clusters. Abused children grow up distrustful, angry, and embittered. Combined with an antisocial orientation and the effects of substance abuse and intoxication, such feelings are likely to be expressed in violent terms.

The cluster E case examples also exhibit a pervasive pattern of aberrant childhood behavior and juvenile criminal activity. In addition, childhood relationships were markedly disturbed, and school problems were common, encompassing not only academic difficulties and truancy but also conduct disturbances. A quantitative analysis of childhood behavior in all cluster E cases is presented in table 7–4. This analysis reveals higher incidences of conduct disturbances and juvenile criminality than were observed in any other cluster.

The analysis demonstrates a universal presence of difficulties in school and interpersonal relations—the most pervasive pattern of this kind found in any cluster. If any cluster's childhood behavior pattern could predict the behavior pattern of adult life, cluster E is certainly that cluster.

The Impact of a Predatory Antisocial Orientation and Substance Abuse

Let us now summarize the salient features that characterize cluster E. Many of the same proximate causes that characterize cluster D also are present here. Interpersonal relations and impulse control are impaired, an antisocial orientation is prominent, active substance abuse problems are invariably present, and intoxication at the time of the crime is very common.

There are important differences between the two clusters, however. Feelings of alienation, while noted in both clusters, are observed to be qualitatively different. In cluster D, such findings are long-standing in some cases and of recent origin in others. In cluster E, such feelings always are rooted in childhood and are more intense. Additionally, borderline and low-impact personality disorders predominate in cluster D, but antisocial personality disorders predominate in cluster E. Cluster E murderers also are likely to deny responsibility for their crimes, while cluster D murderers are not. Exposure to significant stress, which is very important in cluster D, is not a prominent proximate factor in cluster E.

The two clusters also differ demographically. Cluster E murderers are very likely to commit complex crimes and kill strangers, whereas cluster D murderers are likely to commit uncomplicated homicides and kill persons known to them.

Cluster E represents a more antisocial and predatory pattern than does any other cluster. These murderers kill for personal advantage. Only in the prototype are such motives prominent. Whereas cluster D murderers kill without murderous intent because they are intoxicated and have become disorganized due to stress, cluster E murderers commit felonies to gratify their desires and then kill to avoid detection.

What dynamic insight does this cluster demonstrate? First, potential targets are viewed solely as objects whose value is measured only in terms of the pleasure or enrichment they can provide. After being used, they are discarded (often killed) so they cannot identify the assailant. Second, the pervasive antisocial orientation of cluster E murderers virtually ensures that they will not be inhibited by any societal norms. Violence usually is not their aim but rather is a means to an end. It assists in overcoming resistance and/or avoiding detection. Third, cluster E murderers are profoundly alienated and disenfranchised. Their sense of alienation began in childhood, when neglect, deprivation, and/or abuse were rampant and engendered a deep sense of bitterness and rage that increased with time. Fourth, any residual caution or restraint that might have been present to moderate behavior is undone by the presence of active substance abuse, often in association with intoxication. When these residual inhibitions are undone, these individuals conclude that any risk is worth taking. The result is depraved violence.

Of all the clusters we have encountered, cluster E is by far the most dangerous. The victims are usually strangers to the murderers—innocent bystanders caught in the wrong place at the wrong time. Although cluster E murderers constitute a relatively small proportion of the study population, the arbitrariness of their acts and their inclination to choose victims at random and then act with wanton violence causes us to fear them the most.

8
Pure Madness and Homicide

This chapter begins the discussion of the two atypical clusters, clusters F and G. These clusters manifest proximate causal patterns that are decidedly different from that of the prototype. In cluster F, the predominant causal factor is the presence of an incapacitating Axis I psychiatric disorder in the form of psychosis. The impact of psychosis was addressed in the discussion of cluster B, but cluster F murderers lack most of that variant's core factors. Cluster F accounts for only 8 percent of the total study sample, suggesting that some caution about conclusions is warranted. This caution can be tempered, however, given the uniformity of the patterns demonstrated by the cluster.

The Proximate Causal Pattern

Let us begin the discussion of this cluster by introducing two illustrative case examples.

> J.P., a thirty-eight–year–old divorced male, was engaging in mutually consenting but public sexual behavior with a young woman when an innocent bystander encountered the couple. From their appearance and behavior, which was quite bizarre, the victim concluded that the woman was being assaulted. When the victim came to the woman's aid, J.P. stabbed the man in the abdomen, causing his death.
>
> J.P. graduated from high school and for eleven years thereafter lived a functional life, working in state government and ultimately rising to a supervisory position.

Nine years before his crime, his personal and marital life began to unravel. He attributed this to an act of infidelity by his wife, a contention that could not be corroborated and may have been delusional. Alcohol and substance abuse followed transiently, and a severe mental illness emerged. During the next nine years, J.P. underwent a series of psychiatric hospitalizations. He was unable to function at work and ultimately was granted permanent disability status. He insisted that he had experienced a "light experience" or "spiritual transformation" in which a "merging with others, mostly females, my ex-wife, my girlfriend, and other women," occurred. At the same time, feelings of profound sexual inadequacy emerged. A complete change of life-style accompanied these changes, and J.P. began wandering around the United States to fulfill a vaguely-defined religious task that was somehow linked in his mind to John F. Kennedy's assassination.

J.P. was hospitalized on four separate occasions for bizarre behavior. For example, the initial hospitalization occurred after police found J.P. wrapped in a thin piece of material and lying on a sidewalk in subzero temperatures on a midwinter day. The second hospitalization was precipitated by an episode of catatonia during which J.P. remained mute and immobile in a parking lot for several days. In spite of treatment attempts, J.P.'s religious delusions and bizarre behavior persisted. He remained preoccupied with world annihilation fantasies. He became a familiar figure in his community, wandering about wrapped in a sheet that he called a toga and carrying a tree branch that he called his staff. Other hospitalizations followed. On one occasion, J.P. covered his body with green paint, had a club hanging from his wrist, and chanted "Hare Krishna" repeatedly. His response to intermittent treatment with psychiatric medications was poor on the few occasions when he complied with treatment.

J.P.'s crime can be viewed as yet another manifestation of his psychotic disorder. He recalled that on the day of the crime, he encountered a young woman whom he knew from one of his many hospitalizations. He wished to "fulfill scripture with her that day and to take her by this law of capture," by which he meant to act out a delusional ritual that included sexual relations. The ritual was to be performed on the front lawn of a church because J.P. considered it hallowed ground. The psychotic ritual required that the two participants be chained together and that J.P. cut off the woman's hair. It was during this process that the victim happened along and concluded that the woman, who was making loud noises, was being assaulted. The victim intervened, and J.P. responded with violence. Later, by way of explanation, J.P. noted, "He was pulling me away more with his mind than physically. I feel that he intruded on my ritual and hence had to accept the risk." Immediately after stabbing his victim, J.P. said that he knew he "had done something serious. God's going to put me in a harsh judgment." J.P. dropped the knife and became catatonic, the state in which he was found by police.

C.S., thirty-three years old and separated from his wife and children, was working for a public agency when he shot and killed his supervisor. Having carried out this act, he handed his weapon to a coworker and sat down to await the police. Two years earlier, C.S. had come to the conclusion that this supervisor was the devil and had coerced a number of female coworkers into a life of prostitution. He also concluded irrationally that the same man had killed two of C.S.'s friends and was plotting the death of C.S. and his family. C.S. went to the police with his concerns on three occasions during that two-year period, but his allegations went unheeded. When C.S. finally concluded that no one would assist him and that his demise was imminent, he brought a handgun to work. When the supervisor approached C.S., he killed the man.

C.S. was described as a rather unremarkable young man. He graduated from high school and then spent four years in the U.S. Coast Guard, receiving an honorable discharge. C.S.'s progressively worsening psychotic condition began in his early twenties. His difficulties appear to have been associated with his exposure to a film titled *In Search of Dracula.* After viewing the film, C.S. became preoccupied with the mythic figure Dracula and the historical personage Vlad the Impaler, an eastern European ruler on whom the character of Dracula is based.

C.S.'s wife and family accepted this interest as an eccentricity. Therefore, his wife was surprised when C.S. became enraged that she had obtained a personalized license plate for him with the letters VLAD. C.S. felt that his wife had put the family in danger by buying the license plate.

C.S. also exhibited a number of compulsive symptoms. For example, he felt that he had to carry a specific number of rubber bands in each pocket and to cross his fingers and click his heels at particular times and places. Delusional beliefs also emerged. He believed that the numbers on the license plates of passing cars had special significance and communicated information to him, though he was vague about its nature. He confessed to his parents that he thought he was either Christ or God.

When C.S. concluded that his work supervisor had killed two friends, he began describing this man as "the keeper of the keys, also known as the devil." Objective evidence suggested that both friends had simply moved out of the area, but C.S. would not accept this explanation. A brother and other family members found it increasingly difficult to understand C.S.'s commentaries about Dracula and most other things. His wife noted that C.S. would not use his middle fingers and attempted to keep them separated from each other at all times, explaining that they were evil. She returned from work one cold autumn evening and found a suspicious and anxious-looking C.S. on the porch of their home. He had a gun in his hand and their infant in his arms. The child was clad only in a diaper.

As his mental state deteriorated, C.S. began to keep a crowbar in his car and a gun readily accessible at home.

> He accused his wife of engaging in adulterous behavior with her sister and the sister's boyfriend. The accusations, which were false, prompted the first of several separations from his wife.
>
> When C.S. and his wife separated permanently, he installed new locks in the house but was so confused and irrational that the doors could be locked only from the outside. He kept two German shepherds in the house but never walked them, accounting for an increasing amount of fecal matter in the basement. His written and verbal utterances also became less and less understandable. He would mumble to his parents about "the key and the chain to the bottomless pit" and recorded this phrase numerous times in a diary he kept. After committing his crime, C.S. insisted that he had killed the devil and ought to be congratulated not punished.

In both case examples, the murderer reached a totally irrational conclusion about his victim based on delusional thinking and then acted on that delusion. In each case, the impact of psychosis was so profound that it disabled personality functions that might otherwise have inhibited the violent behavior. Moreover, the power of the delusional beliefs was such that each assailant concluded that a violent response was justified or necessary. Neither assailant had any history of prior criminal convictions, and neither had led an antisocial life-style.

A quantitative analysis of proximate causes in all cluster F cases was undertaken, and the results are presented in table 8–1. The data there indicate that baseline mental functions such as interpersonal relations, impulse control, thinking, and reality testing usually were impaired. However, interpersonal relations sometimes were maintained in spite of the intrusion of psychotic symptoms, and impulsive behavior was not noted invariably prior to the homicidal act. For example, C.S. maintained a marital relationship and friendships until shortly before his crime. Impairment of reality testing and thinking was found in all cases. This is not surprising, as such impairment is a hallmark of the psychoses suffered by all cluster F murderers. The only other cluster in which a high incidence of impairment in these two

Table 8–1
Percent of Cluster F Cases and Prototype Cases in Which Specific Proximate Causal Factors Were Present

Proximate Cause Category	*Cluster F (n = 8)*	*Prototype (n = 20)*
Baseline mental functions		
Impaired interpersonal relations	62.5	95.0
Impaired impulse control	62.5	85.0
Impaired reality testing	100.0	0.0
Impaired thinking	100.0	5.0
Impaired cognition	0.0	5.0
Impaired self-image	25.5	5.0
Antisocial values	0.0	75.0
Alienation/disenfranchisement	87.5	75.0
Presence of Axis I symptomatic psychiatric disorders		
Psychoses	100.0	0.0
Psychoneuroses	0.0	5.0
Substance abuse disorders	0.0	0.0
Behavior/organic/mental retardation	0.0	25.0
No Axis I disorder	0.0	70.0
Presence of Axis II personality disorders		
Antisocial personality	0.0	50.0
Borderline, paranoid, schizoid, or schizotypal personality	0.0	35.0
Histrionic or narcissistic personality	0.0	5.0
Low-impact disorders (avoidant, dependent, obsessive-compulsive, or passive-aggressive)	0.0	0.0
No Axis II disorder	100.0	10.0
Presence of substance abuse problems (with or without diagnosis of substance abuse disorder)		
Alcohol abuse only	0.0	5.0
Drug abuse only	12.5	5.0
Both alcohol and drug abuse	0.0	10.0
Presence of transient factors		
Rationalizing or justifying motives	50.0	70.0
Intoxication	0.0	5.0
Significant stress	12.5	40.0

areas was noted is cluster B, which also is characterized by psychotic disorders.

The conclusion that cluster F is one of two atypical clusters is based on the observation that many of the proximate causes associated with the prototype and its variants were not present. An antisocial orientation, so prominent in the prototype, was absent in cluster F. Feelings of alienation and disenfranchisement were common in cluster F but differed from those seen in the prototype. In the latter, such feelings were global in nature and long-standing in duration. In Cluster F, such feelings were linked directly to psychotic disorganization and were absent prior to its emergence.

No cluster F murderer met the criteria for a diagnosis of any personality disorder, a stark departure from the pattern observed in the prototype. Also, rationalizing motives were present in only half the cluster F cases. Even when these motives were present, they did not reflect predatory self-interest as they did in the prototype but invariably were the product of delusional beliefs. Substance abuse, intoxication, and stress, all prominent proximate causes in at least some prototype variants, were not prominent causes in this cluster.

Based on these findings, cluster F murderers manifested the following proximate causal pattern:

1. A majority exhibited impairment of interpersonal relations and impulse control.
2. All exhibited impairment of reality testing and rational thinking.
3. All met the criteria for the diagnosis of an Axis I psychotic disorder.
4. None met the criteria for the diagnosis of an Axis II personality disorder.
5. None demonstrated a failure of socialization or the presence of antisocial values.
6. Half offered rationalizing motives for their crimes, and in every instance those motives were the product of delusional thinking.

This pattern provides Cluster F with its basic causal identity.

The Demographic Pattern

Cluster F's demographic pattern, which is presented in table 8–2, also reflects its atypical status. Note especially the high pro-

Table 8–2
Percent of Cluster F Cases and Prototype Cases in Which Specific Demographic Characteristics Were Present

Demographic Category	*Cluster F (n = 8)*	*Prototype (n = 20)*
Assailant is male	62.5	90.0
Assailant is female	37.5	10.0
Assailant has prior criminal convictions	0.0	65.0
Assailant has no prior criminal convictions	100.0	35.0
Victim is known to assailant	75.0	70.0
Victim is not known to assailant	25.0	30.0
Assailant committed homicide only	100.0	65.0
Assailant committed homicide and rape	0.0	25.0
Assailant committed homicide and robbery	0.0	10.0
Assailant is younger than 18 years old	0.0	5.0
Assailant is 18 to 24 years old	37.5	25.0
Assailant is 25 to 39 years old	62.5	50.0
Assailant is 40 years or older	0.0	20.0
Assailant killed only one victim	87.5	70.0
Assailant killed more than one victim	12.5	30.0

portion of women murderers in this cluster, a finding observed previously only in cluster B. This adds credence to the hypothesis that homicidal behavior in women is primarily the result of psychotic disorganization. Note also the total absence of prior criminal histories or complex crimes, which contrasts to the much higher incidence rates of such crimes in the prototype. Finally, note the absence of very young murderers, which is not surprising since psychoses often do not come to full fruition until late adolescence or early adulthood.

The Long-Term Causal and Childhood Behavior Patterns

To examine long-term causality and childhood behavior in this cluster, let us add to the two case examples.

> J.P. was raised by his mother and grandmother until the age of five, as his parents separated when he was six

months old. His mother then remarried, and a stepfather joined the family. J.P. never got along well with him and harbored unremitting feelings of jealousy. He had no contact with his natural father. J.P. could recall being spanked by his mother for bed-wetting, which persisted until he was nine years old. He was subsequently traumatized by the death of a close friend during adolescence. No other significant childhood traumas or disruptions were reported.

Besides bed-wetting, J.P. manifested sleep and appetite disturbances during childhood, but psychotic symptomatology was not observed during childhood or adolescence. Making friends did not come easily to J.P., but neither conduct disturbances nor juvenile criminality was present during childhood. In addition, no difficulties were noted at school.

C.S.'s childhood background was even less remarkable. He came from an intact family in which both parents held stable and responsible jobs. His relationship with his parents appears to have been satisfactory and uneventful. The parents were still married at the time of C.S.'s crime. No abuse or neglect was reported in the family, and no childhood disruptions were noted. C.S. seemingly had an average middle-class upbringing.

C.S.'s parents described him as a quiet and fearful child. The only manifestations of conduct difficulties involved the use of marijuana and LSD during adolescence. No juvenile criminality was observed. C.S. was described as a lonely child with relatively few friends. His school performance was not stellar, but it was satisfactory.

There was little evidence of childhood trauma in either case example. When all eight cases in the cluster were examined quantitatively, a pattern very different from that of the prototype emerged. The results of this analysis are presented in table 8–3. In all but one of the categories listed in the table, the incidence rates of trauma lag far behind those for the prototype. In the one exception, which relates to instability in the childhood envi-

Table 8–3
Percent of Cluster F Cases and Prototype Cases in Which Specific Long-Term Causal Factors Were Present

Proximate Cause Category	*Cluster F (n = 8)*	*Prototype[a] (n = 20)*
Any negative role models	25.0	55.6
Father had criminal history	0.0	17.6
Father had substance abuse problems	0.0	11.8
Mother had criminal history	0.0	5.3
Mother had substance abuse problems	0.0	26.3
Sibling had criminal history	12.5	31.6
Sibling had substance abuse problems	25.0	36.8
Any instability in childhood environment	75.0	72.2
One parent absent	50.0	68.4
Both parents absent	25.0	10.5
One or both parents died	12.5	5.3
One or more siblings died	0.0	0.0
Father was mentally ill	0.0	5.6
Mother was mentally ill	0.0	10.5
Sibling was mentally ill	25.0	5.3
Parents were divorced	37.5	63.2
Any lack of safety in childhood environment	25.0	73.7
Exposure to physical abuse	12.5	36.8
Exposure to sexual abuse	0.0	5.3
Exposure to pervasive neglect	12.5	63.2
Any disruption in childhood environment	0.0	52.6
Placement in institutional setting	0.0	47.4
Hospitalization in medical setting	0.0	10.5
Hospitalization in psychiatric setting	0.0	10.5

[a]Some missing data for three cases.

ronment, the absence of one or both parents was the predominant source of trauma. In fact, the trauma rates observed in this cluster are even lower than those observed in cluster B, the other cluster in which psychosis plays a prominent role.

The relative lack of childhood trauma should not come as a surprise if we recall the discussion in chapter 4. There it was argued that a genetic component in the etiology of psychosis offsets the need for a great amount of environmental trauma to be present to produce the same result. The incidence rate of mental illness among the siblings of cluster F murderers was five times higher than that noted in the prototype, which lends additional support to this genetic thesis. The fact that the incidence of trauma in this cluster was lower than that in cluster B also is understandable in light of the fact that psychosis and personality dysfunction were the ultimate outcomes in the latter cluster. Psy-

Table 8–4
Percent of Cluster F Cases and Prototype Cases in Which Specific Childhood Behavior Abnormalities Were Present

Proximate Cause Category	*Cluster F (n = 8)*	*Prototype[a] (n = 20)*
Any psychiatric symptoms	25.0	0.0
Speech disorders	0.0	0.0
Phobias	12.5	0.0
Sleep disturbances	12.5	0.0
Eating disturbances	12.5	0.0
Enuresis	12.5	0.0
Encopresis	0.0	0.0
Any disturbances of conduct	12.5	63.2
Fire setting	0.0	10.5
Cruelty to animals	0.0	15.8
Chronic lying	12.5	57.9
Repetitive stealing	0.0	47.4
Acts of vandalism	0.0	31.6
Any criminal behavior	0.0	45.0
Homicide	0.0	0.0
Rape	0.0	5.0
Other sexual crimes	0.0	10.0
Aggravated assault	0.0	25.0
Armed robbery	0.0	15.0
Other violent crimes	0.0	0.0
Property-related crimes	0.0	40.0
Drug-related crimes	0.0	5.0
Any school difficulties	50.0	70.0
Academic problems	50.0	70.0
Truancy problems	25.0	55.0
Any problems with relationships	100.0	94.7
School behavior problems	0.0	35.0
Violent behavior at school	0.0	20.0
Problems relating to father	87.5	84.2
Problems relating to mother	62.5	73.7
Problems relating to siblings	25.0	73.7
Difficulty making friends	37.5	68.4
Difficulty keeping friends	37.5	57.9
Repetitive temper outbursts	12.5	36.8
Chronic disobedience	0.0	57.9

[a]Some missing data for one case.

chosis does not require as significant an environmental contribution, as does personality dysfunction. Hence, clusters A, B, and F exhibit a progressive diminution of environmental trauma. In cluster A, personality disorganization is the primary proximate causal factor, and a high trauma rate would be expected to produce it. In cluster B, both personality disorganization and psychosis are present, which requires both environmental and genetic contributions. Finally, in cluster F, only psychosis is observed; the genetic contribution to it is critical, making environmental trauma less important.

The pattern of childhood behavior in the two case examples indicates that psychiatric symptoms and difficulties with interpersonal relations were present but that conduct disturbances and juvenile criminality were rare or absent. This pattern is corroborated by a quantitative analysis of the eight cases in the cluster (table 8–4). The data in the table reveal that psychiatric symptoms were present in 25 percent of the cases, but conduct disturbances and juvenile criminality were rare or unknown. This is a vastly different pattern from that seen in the prototype, where conduct disturbances and criminality were prominent. Conversely, school difficulties were almost as common in cluster F as in the prototype, and impaired interpersonal relations were even more common in cluster F. These findings contrast with those for cluster B, where psychiatric symptomatology, conduct disturbances, and juvenile criminality all were evident, an expected finding given the mixed pattern of proximate causes in that cluster. Overall, the childhood behavior patterns of the cases in clusters B and F predict the adult patterns quite well.

The Profound Impact of Psychotic Thinking and Beliefs

Let us now summarize the salient features of cluster F. Clearly, the most prominent proximate cause in this cluster is the presence of major psychopathology in the form of psychosis. Impairment based on psychotic symptomatology is so pervasive that it dwarfs all countervailing mental functions that might have thwarted violent behavior. All other proximate causes play a secondary role in this cluster. To be sure, impairment of interpersonal relations and impulse control contributes to the homicidal outcome, but it is not as pervasive as in the prototype. Impairment of reality testing and rational thinking is closely connected to the psychotic process.

Feelings of alienation and/or disenfranchisement occur, but only after the psychosis has taken its toll. Rationalizing motives, when present, are invariably linked to psychotic delusions.

Psychotic disorders contribute to dysfunction and disorganization in three basic ways. First, the disorganization of rational thinking precludes rational deliberation and the application of good judgment. Thinking is muddled, and sensible decision making based on facts becomes difficult or impossible.

Second, the presence of extraordinary psychic pain in the form of extreme anxiety demands relief at any cost. Sometimes this cost takes the form of irrational and violent behavior. This is well illustrated in cases where command hallucinations threaten and cajole psychotic individuals into carrying out instructions. No relief, however transient, is forthcoming until the voices have been obeyed.

Third, there are major distortions of reality. Hallucinations and delusions, common symptoms in psychosis, replace reality with an idiosyncratic view of the world that is not shared by others. Hallucinations and delusions may provide erroneous signs of danger where none really exists. This sense of danger can in turn provoke a violent reaction that is unnecessary in reality but very necessary in the context of the psychosis. This idiosyncratic reality also can provide an apparent motive for a violent response. A common example of this was C.S.'s delusional belief that his supervisor was about to kill him and his family.

One may well ask why homicide caused solely by the impact of psychosis is rather infrequent. First, psychoses afflict no more than 2 percent of the general population. Second, many of the psychotic disorders that do occur are not associated with symptomatology that provokes a violent response. Command hallucinations and paranoid delusions powerful enough to induce violence are rare. It should be kept in mind, however, that pure psychosis and psychosis in combination with personality disorganization, as discussed in chapter 4, were present in more than one-quarter (28 percent) of the study population. This indicates that although most psychotic patients are not violent, many homicidal individuals are psychotic.

9
Nonpsychotic Psychiatric Disorders, Stress, and Homicide

Cluster G is both the smallest and the most enigmatic of the homicide clusters in that neither madness (as characterizes cluster F) nor severe personality dysfunction (as characterizes the prototype and its variants) is present. Rather, two proximate causal factors are prominent in cluster G—the presence of a nonpsychotic Axis I psychiatric disorder and the impact of significant stress. A third proximate cause, active substance abuse, often is present as well. This confluence of significant factors must produce anger of sufficient intensity to induce a homicidal reaction. Rage of such intensity is rare, and as a result, cluster G accounts for only 6 percent of the study population. This cluster's diminutive size, coupled with the diverse nature of its psychiatric diagnoses, requires that caution be exercised in relation to conclusions reached.

The Proximate Causal Pattern

With the above caution in mind, let us begin by reviewing two illustrative case examples.

> J.W., a thirty-seven–year–old woman, worked in the health care field until her marriage. She had no prior criminal history. She met and became intimate with her last husband at the age of thirty-three but did not marry

him until three years later. J.W. killed her husband one year after their marriage. The crime was precipitated by prolonged marital strife.

Prior to meeting her last husband, J.W. had entered into several ill-considered relationships. Precocious sexual activity at age sixteen had led to a teenage pregnancy. That in turn led to marriage to the teenage father. The marriage lasted only a few months. Thirteen years later, J.W. made an equally poor marital choice when she married a man who left her three months later for a homosexual lover.

For the next three years, J.W. dated sporadically and avoided entanglements. She then met and was pursued by her last husband, a professional who wooed her persistently, ultimately overcoming her initial reservations. These reservations were vague, but J.W. could remember that there was something about this suitor that left her uneasy.

The marriage disrupted J.W.'s life. The couple moved to a house located in an isolated rural area with no close neighbors. The husband objected to J.W.'s desire to continue working, and she stopped doing so. Isolated from familiar surroundings, work, and friends, she became despondent. The despondency was aggravated by increasing detachment and lack of interest on the husband's part.

When the couple's house was destroyed by fire, the husband decided that someone was trying to drive them out of the area, and they moved to an even more isolated setting. At that time, the husband bought a small arsenal of firearms. Shortly thereafter, he began to subject J.W. to a repetitive pattern of physical and sexual abuse. According to J.W., this abuse occurred only when the husband was using cocaine. Evidence of the abuse was corroborated by a review of J.W.'s medical records and by the recollections of the few friends who saw her occasionally during this period.

The stress of abuse was augmented by a second stress caused by the husband's open romantic involvement with a female coworker. Recalling that she was the last to know, J.W. experienced feelings of inadequacy and humiliation, and her despondency increased.

Angry, depressed, and humiliated, J.W. finally concluded that she had to abandon the relationship despite a recognition that this would constitute yet another failure in her own mind. On the morning of the crime, J.W.'s husband apparently found a suitcase she had packed. He allegedly threatened to kill her if she attempted to leave. She contended that when he reached for a handgun, she grabbed a rifle and shot him. She continued to fire the weapon until its magazine was empty. She then fired all the bullets from a second weapon into her husband's body. She subsequently called a friend and sat down to await the police. J.W. was distraught and remorseful over what she had done.

R.H., thirty-two years old and divorced, spent his adolescence and adult life working in the grocery business. He was divorced and living with a male roommate at the time of his crime. R.H. was at home when he began discharging a handgun through his bedroom window. Although he denied any recollection of it, he apparently discharged the weapon in the apartment, fatally wounding his roommate. He denied any feelings of malice toward the roommate. R.H. had no prior criminal history.

R.H. was described by those who knew him as a somewhat shy and retiring man who generally related well to others. R.H. did acknowledge a long history of alcohol and amphetamine abuse. For the most part, this abuse was confined to weekends and occasional weekday nights, but it sometimes interfered with work. As a consequence, R.H. attained managerial positions several times, only to be demoted as a consequence of his substance abuse. Although a good provider and loving father, his marriage also was affected by this abuse, and ultimately R.H.'s wife demanded a divorce.

One month prior to his crime, R.H. was fired from his job for violating company policy. He became despondent. On the day of his crime, R.H.'s ex-wife remarried, exacerbating his despondency and forcing him to abandon the fantasy that he and his wife would ultimately reconcile. Intoxicated and angry, R.H. began firing a revolver into the empty lot. Then he apparently began arguing with his roommate. Others heard the argument but not its content. Later, R.H. could not remember the argument at all, but he did fatally wound the roommate. After the incident, R.H. immediately called for assistance and expressed profound remorse.

Both cases are characterized by two proximate causal factors, depression and exposure to multiple stresses. Both J.W. and R.H. suffered from depressive disorders, and J.H. also suffered from a substance abuse problem. In addition, both had been exposed to multiple stresses. J.W. had experienced physical and sexual abuse, an imminent fear of mortal danger, and the humiliation of her husband's infidelity. R.H. had suffered a recent job loss and the loss of hope that a reconciliation with his ex-wife would occur. In J.W.'s case, fear and humiliation turned into rage. In R.H.'s case, loss turned into rage. The rage was directed at its actual target in one case and at a surrogate target in the other.

Neither of these individuals had exhibited an antisocial orientation or had engaged in any prior criminal activity. Each exploded in a single isolated and uncharacteristic outburst of rage. Neither reaction could have been predicted by the assailant's antecedent behavior. Immediately after the outburst, each assailant expressed intense feelings of remorse and guilt.

A quantitative analysis of proximate causes in all six cases in this cluster is presented in table 9–1. This analysis corroborates the portraits painted by the case examples. Impairment of interpersonal relations was observed in five of the six cases, and impulse control was noted to be poor but without any prior instances of associated violence.

In all six cases, some form of Axis I psychiatric disorder was present—in two cases a depressive psychoneurosis, in two others a substance abuse disorder, and in two a conduct disorder. Substance abuse problems were observed in four cases, but intoxication at the time of the crime was less common. In none of the

Table 9–1
Percent of Cluster G Cases and Prototype Cases in Which Specific Proximate Causal Factors Were Present

Proximate Cause Category	*Cluster G (n = 6)*	*Prototype (n = 20)*
Baseline mental functions		
Impaired interpersonal relations	83.3	95.0
Impaired impulse control	83.3	85.0
Impaired reality testing	0.0	0.0
Impaired thinking	0.0	5.0
Impaired cognition	0.0	5.0
Impaired self-image	33.3	5.0
Antisocial values	33.3	75.0
Alienation/disenfranchisement	33.3	75.0
Presence of Axis I symptomatic psychiatric disorders		
Psychoses	0.0	0.0
Psychoneuroses	33.3	5.0
Substance abuse disorders	33.3	0.0
Behavior/organic/mental retardation	33.3	25.0
No Axis I disorder	0.0	70.0
Presence of Axis II personality disorderss		
Antisocial personality	0.0	50.0
Borderline, paranoid, schizoid, or schizotypal personality	0.0	35.0
Histrionic or narcissistic personality	0.0	5.0
Low-impact disorders (avoidant, dependent, obsessive-compulsive, or passive-aggressive)	0.0	0.0
No Axis II disorder	100.0	10.0
Presence of substance abuse problems (with or without diagnosis of substance abuse disorder)		
Alcohol abuse only	16.7	5.0
Drug abuse only	0.0	5.0
Both alcohol and drug abuse	50.0	10.0
Presence of transient factors		
Rationalizing or justifying motives	16.7	70.0
Intoxication	33.3	5.0
Significant stress	83.3	40.0

cases was any Axis II personality disorder diagnosis made. Only two assailants expressed feelings of alienation. In all but one of the six cases, significant stress was present, and in that case intellectual capacity was significantly impaired. The presence of a rationalizing motive was observed in only one case. In two of the cases, responsibility for the crime was denied, and in three others any intent to cause harm was denied. Contrast this pattern with that of the prototype, in which Axis I psychiatric disorders and exposure to stress were uncommon and Axis II psychiatric disorders, antisocial values, and feelings of alienation were very common.

The following factors compose the common pattern of proximate causes in cluster G:

1. Almost all exhibited impairments of interpersonal relations and impulse control.
2. All met the criteria for the diagnosis of an Axis I psychiatric disorder in the form of psychoneurosis, substance abuse, or conduct disorder.
3. Almost all were exposed to significant stresses.
4. Many suffered from a substance abuse problem at the time of their crimes, but most were not intoxicated.
5. None suffered from an Axis II personality disorder.
6. Few exhibited an antisocial orientation or described feelings of alienation or disenfranchisement.

This pattern defines cluster G's proximate causal identity.

The Demographic Pattern

An analysis of this cluster's demographic pattern reveals that it is consonant with the findings that relate to proximate causality. The results of this analysis are presented in table 9–2. As one might expect, cluster G murderers killed persons known to them in all but one case. In no instance did they commit complex crimes such as homicide and rape or homicide and robbery, and none had prior criminal histories. All focused on single targets.

In terms of demographics, the contrast between cluster G and the prototype is very striking, as the prototype's pattern was more pervasively criminal, with a high incidence of prior criminality, a significant proportion of complex crimes, and a higher proportion of victims who were not known to the assailant.

Table 9–2
Percent of Cluster G Cases and Prototype Cases in Which Specific Demographic Characteristics Were Present

Demographic Category	*Cluster G (n = 6)*	*Prototype (n = 20)*
Assailant is male	83.3	90.0
Assailant is female	16.7	10.0
Assailant has prior criminal convictions	0.0	65.0
Assailant has no prior criminal convictions	100.0	35.0
Victim is known to assailant	83.3	70.0
Victim is not known to assailant	16.7	30.0
Assailant committed homicide only	100.0	65.0
Assailant committed homicide and rape	0.0	25.0
Assailant committed homicide and robbery	0.0	10.0
Assailant is younger than 18 years old	33.3	5.0
Assailant is 18 to 24 years old	16.7	25.0
Assailant is 25 to 39 years old	50.0	50.0
Assailant is 40 years or older	0.0	20.0
Assailant killed only one victim	100.0	70.0
Assailant killed more than one victim	0.0	30.0

The Long-Term Causal and Childhood Behavior Patterns

To examine the issues of long-term causality and childhood behavior in this cluster, we must add to the two illustrative case examples.

> J.W. was raised by strict Creole grandparents because her parents had significant substance abuse problems. Neither parent played an important role in her upbringing. Unfortunately, the grandmother died when J.W. was nine years old and the grandfather when she was sixteen, essentially resulting in the loss of parental figures twice during J.W.'s childhood. For a brief period after the grandfather's death, J.W. lived with her father, who made sexual overtures to her, causing J.W. to flee to another relative's home. She had minimal contact with her father after that.

Despite multiple losses, J.W. showed relatively little evidence of impairment during childhood. No psychiatric symptomatology was reported, and J.W. did not manifest juvenile criminal behavior. She did well in school and ultimately graduated from a nondegree nursing program. A teenage pregnancy provided the major hint of future interpersonal difficulties.

R.H. was raised by only one parent. His mother divorced his alcoholic father when he was three years of age, and he had no further contact with his father until adulthood.

Table 9–3
Percent of Cluster G Cases and Prototype Cases in Which Specific Long-Term Causal Factors Were Present

Long-Term Cause Category	*Cluster G*[a] *(n = 6)*	*Prototype*[b] *(n = 20)*
Any negative role models	80.0	55.6
Father had criminal history	20.0	17.6
Father had substance abuse problems	80.0	11.8
Mother had criminal history	0.0	5.3
Mother had substance abuse problems	25.0	26.3
Sibling had criminal history	25.0	31.6
Sibling had substance abuse problems	25.0	36.8
Any instability in childhood environment	100.0	72.2
One parent absent	100.0	68.4
Both parents absent	80.0	10.5
One or both parents died	0.0	5.3
One or more siblings died	0.0	0.0
Father was mentally ill	0.0	5.6
Mother was mentally ill	0.0	10.5
Sibling was mentally ill	0.0	5.3
Parents were divorced	100.0	63.2
Any lack of safety in childhood environment	60.0	73.7
Exposure to physical abuse	20.0	36.8
Exposure to sexual abuse	40.0	5.3
Exposure to pervasive neglect	60.0	63.2
Any disruption in childhood environment	20.0	52.6
Placement in institutional setting	20.0	47.4
Hospitalization in medical setting	0.0	10.5
Hospitalization in psychiatric setting	0.0	10.5

[a]Some missing data for two cases.
[b]Some missing data for three cases.

Table 9–4
Percent of Cluster G Cases and Prototype Cases in Which Specific Childhood Behavior Abnormalities Were Present

Behavior Category	*Cluster G*[a] *(n = 6)*	*Prototype*[a] *(n = 20)*
Any psychiatric symptoms	20.0	0.0
Speech disorders	0.0	0.0
Phobias	20.0	0.0
Sleep disturbances	0.0	0.0
Eating disturbances	0.0	0.0
Enuresis	0.0	0.0
Encopresis	0.0	0.0
Any disturbances of conduct	60.0	63.2
Fire setting	0.0	10.5
Cruelty to animals	0.0	15.8
Chronic lying	60.0	57.9
Repetitive stealing	20.0	47.4
Acts of vandalism	20.0	31.6
Any criminal behavior	16.7	45.0
Homicide	0.0	0.0
Rape	0.0	5.0
Other sexual crimes	0.0	10.0
Aggravated assault	0.0	25.0
Armed robbery	0.0	15.0
Other violent crimes	0.0	0.0
Property-related crimes	16.7	40.0
Drug-related crimes	0.0	5.0
Any school difficulties	50.0	70.0
Academic problems	33.3	70.0
Truancy problems	50.0	55.0
Any problems with relationships	100.0	94.7
School behavior problems	50.0	35.0
Violent behavior at school	0.0	20.0
Problems relating to father	100.0	84.2
Problems relating to mother	40.0	73.7
Problems relating to siblings	40.0	73.7
Difficulty making friends	80.0	68.4
Difficulty keeping friends	80.0	57.9
Repetitive temper outbursts	20.0	36.8
Chronic disobedience	40.0	57.9

[a]Some missing data for one case.

His adult interaction with his father was bitterly disappointing, leaving R.H. despondent about the lost relationship. In other respects, his childhood experiences were unremarkable.

> R.H. did not exhibit psychiatric symptomatology, conduct disturbances, or juvenile criminality during childhood. After graduating from high school, he served four years in the armed services and received an honorable discharge.

These two case examples suggest that childhood trauma is common in this cluster, and a quantitative analysis of long-term causality presented in table 9–3 confirms this view. Parental absence was exceedingly common, as the incidence rate for absence of both parents was 80 percent, almost eight times that noted in the prototype. Exposure to sexual abuse also was very common, again occurring at a rate almost eight times that seen in the prototype.

Little in the way of childhood behavior difficulties was noted in the case examples, but a quantitative analysis of cluster G's childhood behavior pattern (table 9–4) indicates a higher incidence of such dysfunction. Keep in mind that some data are missing for one of the six cases. Disturbances of conduct were observed in three of five cases, school difficulties in three of six cases, and relationship difficulties in all cases. Only criminal behavior and psychiatric symptomatology were rare.

While the childhood histories of these individuals suggest the possibility that some sort of later difficulty might occur, predictions of future homicidal behavior would have been exceedingly difficult to make.

The Impact of Nonpsychotic Psychiatric Disorders and Stress

Let us now summarize the salient features that characterize cluster G. The specific causal pattern that characterizes this cluster is comprised of two proximate causes, the presence of a nonpsychotic Axis I psychiatric disorder and exposure to significant stress. A third key element is a pervasive festering anger that explodes suddenly into an outburst of rage. The festering anger is related to stress, and when this anger is translated into sudden rage, it cannot be contained or expressed appropriately. Equally striking is the absence of proximate causes such as an antisocial orientation, a sense of alienation, rationalizing motives, and Axis II personality disorders.

The nonpsychotic Axis I psychiatric disorders found in this cluster were divided equally among three categories: psychoneurotic depression, conduct disturbances, and substance abuse disorders. All three impede coping capacities. While impulse control was characteristically impaired in these individuals, prior violent outbursts were uncharacteristic.

Stress, often from multiple sources, serves as a trigger, tilting a fragile balance in the direction of violence. Invariably, the stresses observed in these cases involved some kind of loss or rejection. Conflict with friends or parents, the loss of a friend through suicide, marital discord, job loss, and expulsion from school were all noted in the cluster G cases. In the one case in which significant stress was not found, mild developmental disability was present, rendering the assailant less capable of coping with the normal demands of life.

In every case, a sudden outburst of rage was connected to stress. This rage was expressed in violence. The actual object of the anger in this cluster usually becomes its target, but if that object is unavailable, a surrogate target will suffice. Cluster G murderers harbor highly ambivalent feelings toward their victims—a mixture of love and hate, neediness and aversion. After these murderers have expressed their anger in violence, their ambivalence quickly reemerges in feelings of remorse and regret.

It is easy to see why cluster G is the smallest of the seven clusters. To produce a homicidal outcome, exquisite timing is required for the essential causal elements to be operating with sufficient intensity at a time and place when a victim is present. As one can imagine, this confluence of factors rarely occurs.

10
Summation

This chapter summarizes the study findings. Such a summation enables us to answer three of the four questions posed in the introduction to this book. These questions concern which causal factors are responsible for homicidal behavior, whether murderers constitute a homogeneous or heterogeneous group, and, if heterogeneous, whether murderers can be sorted into meaningful clusters.

In answer to the first question, it does appear that the proximate causal factors enumerated in the book can account for the initiation of homicidal behavior. In response to the second question, considerable heterogeneity was observed in the study population. In response to the third question, cluster analysis techniques were successful in identifying a set of seven distinct homicide clusters.

In spite of our ability to cluster murderers, one cannot conclude that heterogeneity reigns exclusively among them. Impairment of interpersonal relations and impulse control is found to be almost universally present in all clusters, and a core set of proximate causes characterizes a prototype cluster and four variants. Together, these five related clusters account for 86 percent of the study population. Only two clusters do not share this common core. The core includes the presence of some type of personality disorder, behavior indicative of antisocial values, and feelings of alienation and/or disenfranchisement. As important as these similarities are, the differences that distinguish these five clusters from each other are even more important.

The first variant, cluster B, is characterized by the presence of severe mental illness in the form of psychosis. Exposure to stress often is a distinguishing feature of this cluster.

In the second variant, cluster C, the shared core is characterized by a less dramatic antisocial orientation. Mental illness in the form of psychoneurosis, impairment of self-image, and evidence of exposure to stress also are present.

In the third variant, cluster D, substance abuse disorders, usually in conjunction with intoxication and often in association with stress, are present.

In the fourth variant, cluster E, substance abuse in association with profound alienation and an especially antisocial and predatory outlook is present.

All these variants share a communal set of proximate causes, but they also exhibit distinct patterns based on the presence, absence, nature, and severity of other specific causal factors.

In the two atypical clusters, decidedly different patterns are present. Cluster F murderers exhibit impairment of reality testing and thinking and other symptoms of psychosis, but the absence of other proximate factors is striking. Cluster G murderers exhibit the symptoms of nonpsychotic psychiatric disorders in association with exposure to stress and, on occasion, substance abuse problems. Here, too, the absence of other core proximate causes is striking.

From the above recapitulation, it is clear that causal factors relevant to the etiology of homicide are identifiable and useful in classifying murderers into distinct clusters.

11
Implications

This chapter delineates the implications of the study findings and examines special issues. In so doing, the fourth question posed in the introduction, whether a better understanding of causality can lead to the enhancement of prediction, prevention, and case management, will be addressed.

Implications of the Study Findings for Predictive Models

As suggested at the outset of this book, the creation of an accurate and reliable predictive model from a retrospective study such as this is an unrealistic expectation. However, the findings could be used to formulate a prospective study that might yield a predictive model. Especially useful in this regard is the set of proximate causes identified and the clusters derived from this set. The study findings also provide several insights that may enhance prediction.

The first insight introduces the model of cumulative causality to the study of homicide. This concept suggests that unless a minimum causal threshold is reached, homicide is an unlikely outcome. As more factors that can contribute to the etiology of a homicidal event occur simultaneously, the likelihood that such an event will occur increases. If only one or two proximate causes are present, the threshold is not reached, and a homicidal event does not occur. If three or more proximate factors are present, however, there is a greater likelihood that such an event will occur. This model is supported by the multicausal proximate factor patterns found in the prototype and its variants, clusters A through E.

A second insight, while initially appearing to contradict the first, is in fact complementary to it and introduces the model of catastrophic causality. This concept suggests that one or two proximate causal factors acting alone can induce a homicidal outcome, but only if these factors have a profound impact on the individual. This model is illustrated by clusters F and G, in which either psychoses or lesser psychiatric disorders in combination with overwhelming stress occur. Note, however, that factors of catastrophic magnitude do not occur often. This observation helps to explain the disparity of incidence rates observed in comparisons between the prototype and its variants and the two atypical clusters. The prototype and its variants epitomize the cumulative model, while the atypical clusters exemplify the catastrophic model.

Ironically, both models are at the mercy of chance. A homicidal outcome always depends on the convergence of necessary circumstances and participants at a single place and time. While certainly not completely accidental, such confluences of factors and participants often rely on the element of chance. Therefore, to some degree, chance limits the potential accuracy of any predictive model.

An important philosophical issue must be addressed in relation to the issue of prediction. It poses the question "To what use would a predictive model be put even if it were accurate and reliable?" Would society resort to preventive detention, for example, on the basis of some predictive assessment? Any society that values freedom of action and holds people accountable for what they do and not for what they might do is severely constrained with respect to the application of any predictive model. For this reason, preventive strategies are more useful than predictive models.

Implications of the Study Findings for Preventive Strategies

It is obviously desirable to reduce the incidence of violent behavior. To do so, one can capitalize on study findings pointing to relevant causes that are both proximate and long-term in nature. Attention to such causes can reduce the incidence of violence. This is true whether we focus on catastrophic events or on the cumulative impact of multiple causes.

Any discussion of preventive strategies must include a range of interventions that can be directed at both proximate and long-term causes. While this study shows that long-term causes have less specific and less direct links to homicidal behavior than proximate causes, the reduction of long-term causes is extremely important nonetheless.

The strategies discussed here may appear to be very straightforward or even mundane. In truth, the measures that could be undertaken to curb violence are not mysterious but are rarely used. Keep in mind that none of the strategies described here comes free of charge; all require an infusion of community resources.

Prevention through Conflict Resolution

Programs that specialize in conflict resolution represent one means for reducing homicidal violence. Such programs can work only if antagonists are identifiable and accessible to intervention. Moreover, the conflict must present at least some possibility for remediation. "Justifying" motives that indicated conflicts were found in 65 percent of all study cases and in 70 to 87 percent of the cases in clusters A through D. Hence, there would appear to be fertile ground for this approach.

Let us look more precisely at the possibilities. In forty-three of the one hundred study cases, victims and assailants were related or were friends. In twenty-four of these forty-three cases, a nonpsychotic motive or a conflict that induced significant stress was present. Hence, in almost one-fourth of all cases, both the assailant and the victim were identifiable and accessible, and some motive or conflict that could respond to mediation efforts was present. Although the motive was not the only proximate cause in these cases, conflict resolution would have reduced the likelihood of the violent outcome.

Conflict resolution or mediation programs could be offered to the public through domestic relations courts, community mental health centers, family service agencies, agencies that provide protective services for children, and health care facilities. They also could be mandated for persons on probation or parole status who have histories of violent behavior.

Prevention through Stress Management

Stress-reduction programs could provide a second prevention strategy. Exposure to significant stress was a prominent causal factor in half of the study cases, and in clusters C and G it was present in 92 percent and 83 percent of cases, respectively. The nature of such stresses ran the gamut from stress-inducing interpersonal conflicts, school and work-related stresses, stresses related to financial or health problems, and stresses related to loss or victimization. In some cases, exposure to multiple stresses was observed, while in others a single stress predominated.

Stress-reduction techniques can be used alone or in association with conflict resolution. The appropriate targets for stress-reduction measures include all those who suffer stresses with which they cannot cope using the problem-solving skills already at hand. Obviously, this includes persons who would not resort to violence as a consequence of exposure to stress, as well as to those who would. Persons with histories of violent responses to stress could be offered priority access to such programs and be encouraged or even required through probation and parole systems to participate in them. Additionally, crisis hot lines could serve as an entry mechanism for persons who are on the brink of being overwhelmed by stress. Unfortunately, hot lines, while still in operation in some communities, are often early casualties of the fiscal cutbacks that have plagued the social services during the past decade.

Prevention through Psychiatric Intervention

The provision of accessible and affordable psychiatric treatment services represents a third prevention strategy. Note that Axis I psychiatric disorders were present in 86 percent of the study cases. Psychotic disorders, especially debilitating in their impact, affected 28 percent of all cases, and in two clusters, B and F, they were present in every case.

Not all psychiatrically impaired individuals recognize their infirmities or comply with the requirements of treatment. Also, not all respond to the treatment that is provided. For example, if all twenty-eight psychotic murderers had received appropriate treatment, 30 percent would in all likelihood have experienced a complete remission of their illnesses, and an additional 40 percent could have been expected to achieve some improvement. Thus, twenty of twenty-eight psychotic murderers would have shown at least some improvement if treated, while eight would have shown none. Whether improvement or even remission would have prevented the homicidal event from occurring in every case is far less certain, but at the very least the probability of a homicidal outcome would have been diminished in twenty cases.

Psychoneurotic disorders were present in 16 percent of all study cases, and in cluster C such a diagnosis was made in all but one case. As these conditions often respond to appropriate treatment, psychiatric intervention for this group would have reduced the likelihood of a homicidal event substantially, especially in cases in which there was no concomitant personality disorder. The availability of treatment services for this kind of individual are in extremely short supply.

Substance abuse disorders were present in 34 percent of the cases but represent a more problematic group. In such disorders, improvement and remission rates are low, at least in the short term. Treatment, even if provided, is less likely to produce rapid remission and to have a substantive impact in reducing the likelihood of a homicidal outcome. Of course, to the degree that such treatment can reduce the frequency with which intoxication occurs, it would have a salutary effect.

A look at the actual treatment experience of the study group is in order if we are to test the proposition that adequate psychiatric treatment can reduce the incidence of homicidal behavior. Only thirteen of the eighty-six study subjects suffering from Axis I psychiatric disorders were receiving treatment services at the time of their crimes. Five of the thirteen were not complying with treatment either by refusing to take prescribed medications or by failing to keep treatment appointments. Three of the thirteen were, in my opinion, receiving incorrect or inadequate treatment. Two others were complying with the correct treatment but failed to respond to that treatment. Only three study subjects who were complying with appropriate treatment and were improving still committed homicidal acts. As has already been stated, the elimination of one proximate cause can never guarantee a nonhomicidal outcome.

Why were so few study subjects receiving psychiatric care? The obvious vehicles for providing psychiatric intervention are found in the private and public psychiatric treatment sectors. Unfortunately, the former is beyond the economic reach of many individuals, including those who commit violent acts. The public psychiatric sector is within the economic reach of such persons, but service availability has been decimated by budget-cutting measures. Substance abuse treatment programs also are not adequately funded.

Even if psychiatric services were more readily available, use of them by potentially violent individuals would by no means be certain. In the past several decades, the mental health statutes of many states have placed a premium on civil liberties to the detriment of mandatory treatment compliance. While the need for this was clear given the abuses of involuntary care during the 1950s and 1960s, there is a price to be paid when a public policy is pursued perhaps too aggressively. That price includes an increment of public violence. It may well be that the pendulum has swung too far in the other direction and that the balance between public safety and personal freedom for the severely mentally ill should be reconsidered.

Prevention through the Provision of Vested Interest

Improving the lives of people so that they come to feel that they have something to lose represents a fourth prevention strategy. Feelings of alienation and the perception of being disenfranchised afflicted 79 percent of the study population and were significant proximate causes in six of the seven clusters. Only in cluster G did few individuals have such feelings or perceptions.

Feelings of alienation and perceptions of disenfranchisement can be recent or long-standing in origin. When recent in origin, they generally are the products of some economic or emotional loss that often is blamed on the homicide victim. Alienation of recent origin was found in thirty-nine of the one hundred study cases and was especially prevalent in clusters C, D, and F. Resolution of such feelings may well have changed the outcome in some of these cases.

Successful intervention in these situations requires that misperceptions about blame be corrected or that actual wrongs be rectified. Only if this is accomplished can the risk to a potential victim be reduced. Such clarification or rectification may not be easy to achieve, but given the potential outcomes, attempts to do so are imperative.

Long-standing feelings of alienation and perceptions of disenfranchisement represent a proximate cause that is likely to be even more resistant to intervention. Many individuals who have these feelings and misperceptions come from an underclass that views the world as a hostile and uncaring place. They generally suffered multiple traumas during childhood and thereafter suffered a chronic lack of success that left them depleted, without resources, hopeless, and embittered. Any society that does not do its utmost to prevent the creation of such an underclass risks an upsurge of lawlessness and violence. It takes only a modicum of common sense to recognize that persons with little or nothing to lose are likely to have fewer constraints on their behavior than persons who do. Persons who feel embittered and cheated are likely to consider violence as a legitimate means to some desired end.

Long-standing alienation and disenfranchisement was found in forty of the one hundred study cases. These feelings generally began in childhood and were self-perpetuating as the person's interpersonal, emotional, and educational skills were permanently stunted. Such feelings were especially prevalent in clusters A and E, which were marked by particularly predatory behavior, and in cluster B, which was marked by both predatory behavior and psychosis. Hence, such feelings were found to be present in individuals who could be considered to be particularly dangerous.

Prevention efforts directed at long-standing alienation and disenfranchisement require major societal investments to expand both skill levels and real opportunities. Empty rhetoric about safety nets falls far short of the mark. Meaningful prevention is no small task in a society plagued by the specter of government insolvency on the one hand and industries that require a work force with ever increasing technical sophistication on the other. It may be difficult or impossible to reverse such alienation in adults, but children may be viable targets of intervention. It is not clear, however, whether our society has the resources, insight, or resolve to address the problem at this time.

Prevention through Restriction of Weapons

It is impossible to control access to all of the various weapons that people use to commit violent acts. However, some weapons have proven to be consistently more lethal than others. Firearms are the most lethal weapons. Proponents of free access to firearms argue that most persons who wish to obtain and use them will do so whatever their legal accessibility. This is undoubtedly true in some instances. Among the study subjects, this contention would apply to many, if not all, of the murderers who committed complex crimes. Although limited access to firearms is a good idea, it would be foolish to conclude that legal impediments would prevent these individuals from obtaining or using them.

Other persons would be far less likely to obtain firearms if they were tightly controlled or legally inaccessible. Among these persons are those who use such weapons impulsively, causing catastrophic effects not by premeditated design but because firearms happen to be at hand. While the absence of firearms would not preclude violent behavior on the part of such persons, it would diminish the lethality of such violence because virtually any other accessible weapon would be less lethal. Especially when homicide is a consequence of an ill-considered and impulsive outburst, the absence of a firearm would reduce the likelihood of a homicidal outcome.

A review of the study findings reveals that firearms were used in forty-six cases. In thirty-nine of these cases, one or more of the following factors also were present: intoxication, exposure to stress, a romantic argument, lack of any rational motive, or a motive based on a paranoid delusional belief. The violent outbursts caused by these proximate causes usually were followed by feelings of regret as soon as calm and reason were restored. A number of case examples provided in this book illustrate the dire consequences that can result when an assailant and a victim cross paths at a time and place when a firearm is readily available. The absence of a firearm could have produced a very different outcome in any or all of these cases. Gun control will not deter predatory criminals, but it may deter homicidal acts by persons who are not predatory criminals.

Prevention by Improving the Quality of the Childhood Growth and Development Experience

The study findings show that subjects frequently were the victims of some kind of neglect or trauma during childhood. Whether in the form of exposure to negative role models, instability, a lack of safety, or disruptions in the childhood environment, the incidence of trauma was substantial in many cases. Common sense suggests that the etiological roots of the impairment of interpersonal relations, impulse control, and self-image and the precursors of alienation and antisocial values can be found in traumatic childhood experiences. Unfortunately, the study could not provide direct links between specific childhood traumas and adult behavior patterns. Such connections are too complex to discern in a retrospective study, but the fact remains that traumatic childhood experiences are prevalent among murderers.

The price of ignoring childhood trauma includes homicidal violence. To correct this problem, society must invest in future generations from birth. This is not currently happening. Can one think of any area of human skill development that is given shorter shrift than child rearing? Society now expends more resources to enhance the driving proficiency of adolescents than it does their future child rearing capacities. The assumption that such abilities will evolve automatically is illogical, even if we were talking about a group of youngsters whose childhood experiences were essentially sound. Society also does not focus much attention on young parents with demonstrable parental inadequacies. When, as a last resort, child rearing is turned over to a surrogate, an already-traumatized child is likely to be placed into circumstances that are as bad as, and sometimes worse than, the situation from which that child was removed.

The caseloads of child protective services workers who investigate abusive situations are unmanageably high. Shelters and juvenile detention facilities that serve traumatized and dysfunctional children are poorly supported, programmatically inadequate, and often dangerous. Also, treatment and prevention services that could be offered by health care establishments generally are the first to be eliminated when budgets are cut.

Our failure to invest in children and adolescents has been monumental, and this inevitably leads to new generations of adults who are maladapted in some way and may be prone to violence. Such neglect is distressing and ironic because we know a great deal about children's basic developmental needs. Normal growth and development is not a mysterious process. We are not failing for lack of knowledge but rather for lack of investment.

Implications of the Study Findings for Case Management

In cases where homicidal behavior cannot be prevented, an appropriate case management plan should be determined. The issue of case management must be addressed because some individuals who have killed ultimately will be returned to the community. The issue of appropriate management also must be considered if we are to remain a humane society. There are three general approaches to the issue of management: punishment, control, and treatment.

Punitive dispositions raise philosophical rather than scientific questions. "What is the appropriate societal response to extreme antisocial behavior?" is a question better put to philosophers, jurists, and lawmakers than to psychiatrists. Punishment options range in severity from incarceration to capital punishment. Judicial systems mete out punitive responses based on the special circumstances of each homicidal act. For example, in California only homicidal offenders who carry out "murders with special circumstances" can be sentenced to death, and even in such cases, an alternative punishment of "life imprisonment without benefit of parole" can be imposed. It is not appropriate to pursue the issue of punishment at great length in this book, but I believe that punishment should be addressed from a moral and legal perspective rather than a psychiatric one.

Control, the second approach to management, is germane to a psychiatric perspective. Although control does share one characteristic with punishment—the use of confinement—there is an important difference. When confinement is used in connection with control, its aim is the imposition of structure not punishment. From a psychiatric point of view, control or structure must be imposed whenever an individual demonstrates an inability to avoid behavior that jeopardizes that individual or others. The psychological well-being of dangerous individuals, not to mention that of their potential victims, is threatened if the need for structure is perceived by society but not imposed. Both victims and assailants are psychologically damaged by violence.

The choice among available structural options is a relevant issue in any discussion of control. If the sole aim of control is constraint, a broad range of options may suffice. If, however, the aim also includes treatment for the purpose of modifying personality functioning to reduce the threat of future danger, the options are more limited. Some settings are more therapeutic than others in terms of both resources and attitudes. We must also take into account that not all dangerous persons are suitable subjects for therapeutic intervention. For this reason, not all management options need to be considered in all cases.

The third case management option is treatment. In this era of scarce resources, treatment should be reserved for dangerous individuals whose potential for change is assessed to be substantial. The aim of such therapeutic interventions is to modify an individual's psychological functioning so that future behavior is likely to be less impulsive, antisocial, and maladaptive. Although therapeutic efforts are unlikely to modify values, they can enhance internal control mechanisms, which in turn can control behavior. Individuals who retain antisocial values but see the pragmatic value of controlling behavior and have control mechanisms at their disposal are likely to be less dangerous than those who lack such controls.

While it is possible to carry out treatment in any setting,

some settings are more conducive to therapeutic efforts than others. For instance, penal settings, especially those with prominent punishment orientations, are less conducive and, as a practical matter, have less therapeutic resources than health care settings. Every therapeutic setting that intervenes with dangerous individuals must impose clear standards of behavior and adequate levels of control. It is not necessary or therapeutically desirable, however, for such settings to make life as uncomfortable as possible for offenders. Creating therapeutic environments with optimal conditions for success is critical for society because it will maximize any investment of resources.

The study findings suggest that from a case management perspective, different clusters of murderers require different interventions based on different etiological considerations. For example, cluster A murderers, plagued by feelings of alienation and disenfranchisement, antisocial values, and a high incidence of personality disorders, require therapeutic efforts that focus on enhancing behavioral controls and social and occupational skills. If treatment is successful, such individuals are unlikely to change their values, but they will begin to anticipate the consequences of violent outburts and can come to feel that these consequences outweigh their momentary benefits. Intervention with this cluster should involve techniques that enhance socialization skills rather than those that provide abstract psychological insights.

Society's success with cluster A murderers will depend not only on therapeutic outcome but also on the economic health of the community, which must be able to offer viable opportunities to persons with newfound educational and occupational skills. If such skills do not lead to gainful employment, their acquisition will be seen as further evidence of how society has cheated them. This, in turn, will lead to more antisocial activity, which may include violence. When such individuals are returned to the community, close supervision is necessary for prolonged periods to augment the shaky socialization skills now in place.

Cluster B murderers require the same kind of therapeutic interventions as cluster A murderers, but their psychotic disorders also must be treated with psychopharmacologic and psychotherapeutic measures. Moreover, since treatment compliance often is poor in this group, continued treatment must be mandated as a condition of community placement. Because psychotic disorders are chronic and incurable, lifelong treatment for them must be imposed. Without such treatment, periodic violence can be expected in at least some of these cases.

Cluster C murderers require all of the therapeutic efforts required by prototypical murderers but also would benefit from psychiatric treatment directed at their psychoneurotic disorders. This may include both psychotherapeutic and psychopharmacologic efforts. While psychoneurotic disorders are generally less incapacitating than psychotic disorders, their presence does affect the tenuous balance of factors that can lead to homicidal outcomes. Stress-reduction techniques should be taught to this group, given the importance of that proximate causal factor in the cluster.

Cluster D murderers require a therapeutic regimen similar to that for cluster C, but instead of psychoneuroses, substance abuse disorders become the primary focus. These disorders do not respond easily to treatment, and even if interventions are successful, improvement does not come quickly and relapses are common. When such individuals are returned to the community, monitoring efforts such as unscheduled urine tests for alcohol and illicit drugs are imperative. Such testing may serve as a deterrent to substance abuse and as an early warning signal.

Cluster E murderers represent a very special group in which the outlook is dire and the need for caution paramount. This cluster's antisocial orientation, extreme predatory outlook, and pattern of substance abuse are causes for great concern. This is the cluster least likely to respond to any sort of therapeutic intervention. The deep-seated antisocial orientation and predatory outlook predict an unremitting pattern of continued violence. Prolonged, if not permanent, confinement for this group is the only means available for ensuring the safety of others. No form of therapeutic intervention currently available is likely to change this cluster's behavior patterns.

In cluster F, the predominant causal factor is psychotic disorganization, so the treatment regimen must address the psychotic symptomatology. Psychotherapeutic measures may prove useful here, but the primary treatment approach must be psychopharmacologic, relying heavily on antipsychotic medications.

If such treatment is successful, confinement for the purpose of control becomes unnecessary and the violence potential drops precipitously. It must be remembered, however, that only 30 percent of psychotic patients respond to treatment with complete remission, while 40 percent experience partial remission, and 30 percent no improvement at all. Thus, some dangerous and psychotic individuals will require lifelong confinement to minimize their risk to the community.

Not all cluster F individuals who can respond to treatment will comply with its requirements. Compliance with treatment, whether voluntary or involuntary, is essential if future violence is to be prevented. When such individuals are returned to the community, compliance with treatment should be made a condition of parole, and treatment status must be monitored closely. Persons who initially were cooperative may cease cooperation after their release. Treatment facilities cannot impose compliance, but parole authorities can and must.

Cluster G murderers suffer from nonpsychotic psychiatric disorders that are exacerbated by stress. A combination of appropriate treatment for the diagnosed disorder and instruction in stress-management techniques is the best approach for these individuals. Also keep in mind that these individuals generally do not represent high risks for future violence once they have committed their crimes. Homicidal behavior in this cluster represents very uncharacteristic behavior. Singular violent outbursts directed at very specific targets who are not easily interchangeable is the pattern. Generally, treatment rather than confinement is the most resource-efficient approach to persons in this cluster, but it is hardly likely to receive community support. Because these individuals are plagued by remorse and guilt, court-mandated community service could serve a particularly useful therapeutic purpose.

Implications of Study Findings for Categorical Groups of Special Interest

Three categorical groups have been identified for special study: female murderers, because women so infrequently commit homicide and are of great interest when they do; murderers who commit complex crimes (homicide and rape or homicide and robbery), because such crimes are particularly heinous and generate special concern; and murderers who kill total strangers, because such criminals strike in apparently random fashion and stimulate our worst fears of helplessness.

Distinctions Based on Assailant's Sex

It has long been observed that women kill infrequently, and it is commonly thought that they do so only when suffering from some severe psychiatric disturbance. This thesis is supported by the study findings.

There were twelve women in the study sample, a proportion quite comparable to that found in the universe of all murderers. Eight of the women (66.7 percent) met the criteria for a diagnosis of some form of psychosis, in contrast to the corresponding rate of psychotic disorders among the men studied (23.9 percent). Four of the eight psychotic women also suffered from personality disorders. Of the four women who exhibited no evidence of psychosis, one was diagnosed as psychoneurotic, a second manifested the symptoms of a conduct disturbance, a third met the criteria for a substance abuse disorder, and a fourth was unafflicted by any psychiatric disorder.

Women murderers also can be distinguished from their male counterparts on the basis of whom they murder. These distinctions are summarized in table 11–1. In most instances, women killed those with whom they had a close relationship. Only

Table 11–1
The Choice of Victim as a Function of Assailant's Sex

	Sex of Assailant	
Relationship of Assailant to Victim	*Male (n = 88)*	*Female (n = 12)*
Family member, boyfriend, or girlfriend	38.6%	75.0%
Neighbor or acquaintance	25.0%	16.7%
Stranger	36.4%	8.3%

rarely did they kill strangers. In contrast, more than one-third of the victims of male murderers were strangers.

For women, therefore, homicide is a personal act often directed against a loved one and usually associated with the presence of severe mental illness. Men murder a far more diverse range of victims, and their homicidal behavior is associated with a broader array of proximate causes.

Distinctions Based on Crime Pattern

Twenty-one of the one hundred study subjects committed complex crimes, either homicide and rape or homicide and robbery. These cases were not evenly distributed among the clusters. Rather, most of the complex cases were found in only two clusters (A and E), and four others were devoid of such cases. Not surprisingly, cluster E, which comprises the most antisocial and predatory individuals, accounted for twelve (56.5 percent) of the complex crime cases. Cluster A, the prototype cluster, which is only somewhat less predatory in nature than cluster E, accounted for seven (33.3 percent) additional cases. Cluster D, with fewer antisocial proclivities, accounted for the last two (9.5 percent) cases. None of the individuals in the clusters associated with psychotic or psychoneurotic disorders committed complex crimes.

These findings demonstrate that complex crimes are associated only with the most antisocial murderers and that substance abuse plays an important role in the genesis of some of these crimes.

Distinctions Based on the Relationship between the Assailant and the Victim

Antisocial proclivities and substance abuse are associated with particular assailant-victim relationship patterns. This association is summarized in table 11–2. Among assailants who killed family members or friends, almost two-thirds fell into clusters associated with psychoses or psychoneuroses and only one-third into clusters marked by an antisocial orientation, often in association with substance abuse problems. Conversely, when assailants and

Table 11–2
Homicide Patterns in Relation to the Choice of Victim

	Relationship of Assailant to Victim		
Cluster Distribution	*Family member, Boyfriend, or Girlfriend (n = 43)*	*Neighbor or Acquaintance (n = 24)*	*Stranger (n = 33)*
Clusters associated with antisocial proclivities with or without substance abuse (clusters A, D, and E)	34.9%	58.3%	72.7%
Clusters associated with psychoses or psychoneuroses (clusters B, C, F, and G)	65.1%	41.7%	27.3%

victims did not know each other, an opposite pattern was observed. When assailants and victims were casually acquainted or lived in proximity to one another, an intermediate cluster distribution was observed.

These findings indicate that the threat of random violence comes not from all murderers but from the specific subset of murderers who are more antisocial and often also afflicted by substance abuse problems.

Implications of the Study Findings with Respect to Conflicts between Psychiatry and the Law

Interactions between psychiatry and the law have received considerable clinical, judicial, and media attention. One aspect of that interaction, the so-called insanity defense, has been especially fraught with confusion and misunderstanding. Dissatisfaction with the insanity defense comes from many quarters, and in recent years, both jurists and the American Psychiatric Association have advocated its abolition. Some have attacked this defense because it excludes too many criminals from accountability, while other critics have reached the opposite conclusion.

Why is this such a contentious subject? First, psychiatric and legal concepts about the nature of human behavior differ in fundamental ways. The prevailing legal view of behavior assumes that free will and the ability to choose freely between courses of action is a basic attribute of adults that is absent in extreme and unusual circumstances. On the basis of this view, most persons should be held accountable for their behavior most of the time.

The prevailing psychiatric view assumes that human behavior is the product of far more complex processes, some of them antithetical to the concepts of free will and freedom of choice. Modern psychiatric theory views more behavior as being beyond an individual's volitional control than the law's behavioral model would assume. On the basis of this view, the issue of accountability becomes far more complex.

As if these differences were not enough, jurists have formulated, with little or no psychiatric input, a number of legal standards for criminal insanity. These standards are used in different jurisdictions. They are contradictory and often vaguely defined. These standards adhere to the basic legal concept of behavior and expect that any psychiatric contribution to the legal process will adapt accordingly, or they ignore the basic conceptual differences between psychiatry and the law and hope for the best. Both approaches fail, and inevitably conflict is generated between psychiatrists and lawyers.

The conflict can be illuminated by examining two different legal standards. The McNaughton standard[30] is consistent with the legal concept of behavior and remains the most commonly used rule for testing sanity. It relies on two measures—whether a defendant knows the nature and quality of his or her act and whether he or she knows that the act is wrong. This standard, now more than one hundred years old, ignores most of what modern psychiatry has discovered about the impact of psychopathology on behavior. A more timely standard, the Durham rule,[31] ignores the basic conceptual differences between psychiatry and the law. It states that if a mental disorder is diagnosed, an individual is legally insane and is relieved of responsibility for his or her act. This standard does not recognize the fact that mental illness encompasses a wide range of conditions with widely varying losses of volitional control.

Let us apply each of these standards to two of the study subjects. Recall J.P., the man who killed an innocent bystander who interrupted J.P.'s public sexual interaction with a female friend (see chapter 8). J.P.'s violence was related to complex irrational delusional beliefs, which were the product of a psychotic disorder. Using the McNaughton standard, a jury found J.P. legally sane because he knew the nature and quality of his act and also knew that it was wrong. Using the Durham standard, the same jury may well have found J.P. legally insane, as he clearly suffered from a severe mental disorder. The difference in outcome would not have been a function of the psychiatric information at hand but rather a function of the different judicial definitions of insanity.

Also consider the case of J.J., who murdered a man who allegedly failed to pay his drug debts (see chapter 3). In J.J.'s case, the only psychiatric diagnosis was that of antisocial personality disorder, a legitimate Axis II psychiatric condition. Again a jury found J.J. sane using the McNaughton standard but could have found him to be insane had it been asked to apply the Durham standard instead.

These two cases, so vastly different psychiatrically, yielded the same results based on one judicial standard and could well have yielded a different but comparable result if a different standard had been applied. To take this matter one step further, had the second jury used the Durham standard and the first the McNaughton standard, J.J., suffering from an antisocial personality disorder, would have been found legally insane, and J.P., suffering from a psychosis, would have been found legally sane. Such an outcome would have defied all reason.

Both legal tests for insanity ignore what is currently known about the impact of psychopathology on behavior. The choice between these standards is based not on scientific knowledge but on social aims. The McNaughton standard is chosen when society through its judicial system desires to hold virtually everyone responsible, and the Durham standard is used when the aim is to hold almost no one responsible. Clearly, neither of these aims is ideal. Instead of using existing judicial standards, which essentially preordain almost every outcome, society, through its lawmakers, could decide which psychiatric disorders it wished to exclude from accountability. For example, individuals with psychotic disorders like J.P. might be considered for exclusion, but predatory and antisocial individuals like J.J. might be held accountable.

Moreover, psychiatric evaluation could be removed from the adversarial arena by restricting all such evaluations to court-appointed evaluators with suitable credentials. Psychiatric evaluators could be asked to diagnose mental disorders using only accepted diagnostic criteria. I believe that such an approach is feasible. While great differences in psychiatric opinion are seen in court testimony, far fewer differences, usually quite circumscribed in nature, are observed in psychiatric practice. A likely reason for this is that the latter situations do not take place in an adversarial environment.

Those who wish to exclude all psychiatric testimony from the judicial process are misguided. It makes little sense to act as if we knew nothing about the factors that affect human behavior. Alternatively, using psychiatric testimony to promote particular social aims also would be misguided. Promoting social aims under the guise of providing impartial information is never appropriate.

Some Final Thoughts

I believe that the study findings add to an understanding of homicidal behavior. First and foremost, they suggest a set of relevant proximate causes. Second, they demonstrate a lack of homogeneity among murderers. Third, they offer a set of clusters that can categorize murderers in terms of proximate causality. Fourth, they offer preventive and case management options for these clusters. Even if future research assigns different proportions of the homicidal population to the clusters, the cluster definitions should retain their validity. The findings also should disabuse any reader of the notion that any single strategy will solve all of society's violence problems.

It is imperative to recognize that the study findings represent only a beginning with respect to the research efforts that should be undertaken in this area. Larger studies drawn from a broader geographic base should be undertaken to corroborate, refute, or modify the findings presented here. Other types of studies, including prospective studies that introduce interventions and then study their impact, also should be undertaken.

This study has examined only one type of violence, homicide. Other types of criminal violence include aggravated assault, rape, and armed robbery. Some forms of violence do not come to the attention of the criminal justice system at all. These forms, though harder to study, deserve scrutiny as well. My hope is that this study will provoke thought, controversy, and consternation and that these reactions in turn will lead to more investigation into this important but relatively neglected subject.

Appendix A: Relevant Sample Selection Issues and Methodological Considerations

This appendix provides greater detail about the methodology described in chapter 3.

Data Sources

I studied one hundred men and women charged with homicide who were referred to me for psychiatric evaluation by judges or attorneys between January 1, 1980, and December 31, 1988. These subjects constituted a subset of a larger referral population of 219 subjects charged with major violent offenses (homicide, aggravated assault, rape, or armed robbery). Excluded from the study were two persons charged with homicide for whom the issue of culpability remained in doubt.

I examined each study subject directly. The minimum number of hours spent with each defendant was four and the maximum in excess of one hundred. I also interviewed other relevant persons, including family members, friends, employers, teachers, therapists, and crime scene witnesses, whenever possible. Data gathered from such persons were used to enhance my understanding of both the crime and the defendant and to corroborate or refute statements made by the defendant.

I also assessed all relevant records provided by defense or prosecuting attorneys. These included military, educational, and medical records, as well as records of prior psychiatric evaluations and treatments. In addition, I examined police reports relating to the crimes, transcripts, audiotapes, and videotapes of police interviews of witnesses and interrogations of defendants; and records relating to the defendants' prior criminal activities.

The Nature of the Sample

The study was not based on random sampling procedures, as cases were referred for study on a nonrandom basis. It was, therefore, imperative to compare the study subjects with the larger universe of murderers from which they were drawn to determine any biases in the sample. The larger universe was defined as all persons who committed homicides in California during the study period (1980 through 1988). Data reflecting the age, sex, race, and ethnic status of murderers, as well as data reflecting the relationship between assailants and victims, were available for this universe. Data for the years 1982 and 1987 were used for comparison purposes.[32,33] The results of this comparison are summarized in table A–1.

In most respects, the demographic profile of the county from which most of the study subjects came did not differ appreciably from that of the state of California, and in such instances no adjustments to the state comparative data were necessary. This was not the case with respect to the Hispanic population, where adjustment was necessary. The county contributing most of the study subjects had a much smaller proportion of Hispanics than did the state population as a whole. As a consequence, this county could be expected to generate proportionately fewer Hispanic murderers than would the total state population. Hence, there was a need to adjust the statewide comparative homicide data to reflect this population difference. The comparative data for Hispanics in table A–1 estimate the number of Hispanic murderers that would be expected in the state universe if the state and county populations of Hispanics had been comparable.

The data in table A–1 indicate that, at least in terms of the measures available for comparison, the study subjects were quite representative of the total universe of murderers.

Table A–1
Demographic Comparisons between Study Subjects and All Murderers in the Study Universe
(percent)

Demographic Categories	*Study Subjects (n = 100)*	*All Convicted Murderers in California, 1982 and 1987*[a]
Age		
Younger than 25 years	33.0%	40.0%
Younger than 40 years	85.0%	85.9%
Sex		
Male	88.0%	89.6%
Female	12.0%	10.4%
Race		
Caucasian	68.0%	58.3%
Black	30.0%	37.1%
Ethnicity		
Hispanic	12.0%	12.3%[b]
Assailant/victim relationship		
Spouse	13.0%	8.4%
Neighbor, friend, or acquaintance	40.0%	50.8%
Parent/child	7.0%	5.8%
Stranger	32.0%	27.5%
Others	8.0%	7.8%

[a]Two-year average.
[b]Adjusted (see text).

Validation of Data

No information obtained from any source was used in subsequent analyses unless it was validated by a reliable independent and unbiased source. This is especially important in evaluations of criminal defendants. In such cases, individuals providing information often had some vested interest in the outcome of an evaluation. For example, a study subject's own report of clinical symptomatology that was not supported by an appropriate form of corroboration was not considered sufficient for making a diagnostic assessment. Corroboration could come from antecedent psychiatric records or a prior therapist's recollections or from observations made by some other reliable observer.

Assessments of substance abuse and intoxication also required validation independent of the defendant's statements. To substantiate the presence of current substance abuse, I sought documentation in medical, psychiatric, or substance abuse treatment records; physical evidence such as needle tracks or the results of a blood or urine analysis; or reliable history from persons knowledgeable about the defendant. With respect to intoxication, I accepted as substantiation the results of a urine or blood analysis conducted in close temporal proximity to the homicide (within two hours) or unequivocal observations by reliable witnesses to the crime coupled with a documented history of active substance abuse.

For purposes of this study, active substance abuse was defined as use on three or more occasions during the month prior to the homicidal event. The definitions of intoxication were appropriated from the third edition of the American Psychiatric Association's *Diagnostic and Statistical Manual*, diagnostic codes 303.00, 305.20–305.70, and 305.90.[34] These codes define intoxication for alcohol, sympathomimetics, cannabis, cocaine, hallucinogens, inhalants, opiates, phencyclidine (PCP), and hypnotics.

Organization of Data

All of the findings were recorded initially as case notes. These notes and their supporting materials were used as the data source for completion of a 229-item questionnaire (see appendix B) that provided a uniform record of relevant demographic, psychiatric, substance abuse, stress, developmental, educational, marital, criminal, and military service information for each defendant. The data from these questionnaires were then stored in computer files and accessed for statistical analyses.

Use of Psychiatric Diagnostic Standards

For the purpose of assigning psychiatric diagnoses to study subjects, I adhered to the diagnostic criteria contained in the third edition of the American Psychiatric Association's *Diagnostic and*

Statistical Manual. Although the revised version of the third edition of this manual was published during the study period, I chose not to use it in order to ensure the continuity of my diagnoses.

Study subjects were assigned no more than one Axis I and one Axis II diagnosis. Where more than one diagnosis could be entertained, the diagnosis judged to be causing the greatest degree of functional impairment was chosen. This approach, rather than the assignment of multiple diagnoses, was used because multiple diagnostic assignments would have led to insurmountable data analysis problems. Moreover, since the data questionnaire allowed for all symptomatology and all drug and alcohol abuse patterns to be recorded, no relevant psychiatric information was lost. Axis I and Axis II diagnoses were made independently of one another, keeping in mind any Axis I diagnosis that would preclude a particular Axis II diagnosis.

During the data analysis phase of the investigation, some diagnoses were aggregated into broader diagnostic categories. This was done to enhance the overall clarity of the data and to create data cells large enough for statistical analyses. All substance abuse diagnoses were categorized together. Schizophrenia, paranoid states, and all affective psychoses were categorized under the label *psychoses.* Organic brain syndromes, mental retardation, and behavioral diagnoses such as sexual sadism and explosive disorders were categorized under the label *behavior/organic/mental retardation.* All psychoneuroses were categorized together.

Among Axis II diagnoses, the borderline, paranoid, schizoid, and schizotypal personality disorders were categorized together. Histrionic and narcissistic personality disorders were categorized together. Avoidant, dependent, compulsive, and passive-aggressive personality disorders were categorized together under the label *low-impact disorders.* The rationale for the various aggregations can be found in appendix C.

It was not feasible for me to invite other clinicians to make independent diagnostic ratings for each subject to examine the issue of interrater reliability. While potentially useful, such an approach was impossible given economic constraints and the constraints imposed by the confidential nature of the forensic evaluations. However, other clinicians were consulted in selected cases. Psychological testing was used in all cases where unresolved clinical diagnostic questions were raised and in all cases where there was a possibility of organic impairment. Medical assessments were requested whenever there was any indication that a medical illness might be contributing to the diagnostic picture. Also, neurological evaluations, including diagnostic tests such as electroencephalograms (EEGs), computerized axial tomographic (CAT) scans, and magnetic resonance imaging scans (MRIs) whenever appropriate.

Statistical Support

All data analyses were conducted using Systat,[35] a statistical program for microcomputers. Systat is highly regarded by statisticians and researchers for the accuracy of its computations and the range of its analyses. Three kinds of analyses were used.

Tabulations and Cross-Tabulations

The Tables Module of Systat was used to provide the basic data sets from which all the numerical data for tables 3–1 through 9–4 were derived. Such analyses are basic to any inquiry of this kind and should require no additional discussion here.

Correlations

The Correlation Module of Systat was used to produce a dissimilarity matrix for use in the cluster analysis. This matrix is described in more detail in the next section.

Cluster Analysis

The Cluster Module of Systat was used to create clusters. Cluster analysis is the name given to a set of statistical techniques that can be used to create classifications. These techniques form clusters, or groups of objects or cases, that share highly similar sets of characteristics. In essence, cluster analysis is a multivariate statistical procedure that takes a uniform set of data variables for a sample of objects or cases and reorganizes them into relatively homogeneous groups on the basis of the data variables.

Cluster techniques are particularly useful for developing typologies based on relevant observations or measurements made for a given group of objects or cases. As Aldenderfer and Blashfield[36] have pointed out, however, the following caveats must be kept in mind when using these techniques:

- Cluster analysis techniques, while relatively simple and straightforward, are not yet supported by a theoretical statistical underpinning such as that developed for analysis of variance or regression analysis techniques.
- Cluster analysis techniques are to some degree inbred in that they may contain some of the biases present in the disciplines for which they have been developed and from which they have evolved.
- Different clustering methods can generate different solutions. In other words, different techniques may separate the same set of cases into clusters with somewhat different elements.

Despite these problems, cluster techniques have proven to be very useful. It is important to judge the usefulness of any solution by the degree to which the established clusters appear to make both empirical and theoretical sense in the context of the problem under study. The work of Aldenderfer and Blashfield, as well as that of Romesburg[37] and the seminal work of Anderberg,[38] can provide the uninitiated reader with a good understanding of this technique. The specific cluster analysis techniques used to create clusters A through G in this study are discussed in the following paragraphs.

Step 1. All of the proximal causal factors enumerated in table 1–1 were coded. All factors except the diagnostic items were coded 1 for impaired and 0 for unimpaired status. Each of the diagnostic items was coded 1 for present or 0 for absent. Each of the one hundred cases in the study sample was then assigned one set of twenty-four response codes, with each set consisting of a series of 0's and 1's.

Step 2. The rectangular data set derived in step 1, a matrix of one hundred cases each containing twenty-four items, was used as the basic data set. The Correlation Module of Systat was then used to compute a simple matching dichotomy coefficient for every pair of study subjects. Such coefficients are similar to the familiar Pearson correlation coefficients and in effect provide a measure of how similar each study subject is to every other study subject. Simple matching dichotomy coefficients are different from Pearson coefficients in that they compare study subjects on the basis of dichotomous rather than continuous variables. The simple matching dichotomy coefficient (a value between 0 and 24) equals $A + D / A + B + C + D$. In this equation, A equals the sum of the variables that have a value of 1 for both study subjects being compared; B equals the sum of the variables in which the first subject being compared has a value of 0 and the second subject a value of 1; C equals the sum of the variables for which the first study subject has a value of 1 and the second subject has a value of 0; and D equals the sum of the variables for which both study subjects have a value of 0. For each pair, $A + B + C + D = 24$. When these simple matching dichotomy coefficients were computed, a one hundred-case by one hundred-case triangular data matrix was produced.

Step 3. The triangular data matrix was then subjected to cluster analysis. The JOIN technique, available in the Systat Cluster Analysis Module, was used. The technique uses the complete linkage criteria and produces a tree, or dendrogram. Such trees contain a unique ordering of cases such that the most similar cases are clustered closest to each other and those least similar farthest apart. The defining rule of complete linkage states that for a case to be included in an existing cluster, it must be within a certain level of similarity to all members of that cluster. Use of the complete linkage criteria tends to create compact clusters comprising highly similar cases.

Step 4. The tree, or dendrogram, must then be interpreted. To do this, an appropriate level of consolidation for establishing clusters is selected. Trees are arranged so that all the study subjects are listed as separate branches on one side, with the most similar cases clustered closest to each other. On the opposite side of the tree are all the cases consolidated into a single trunk. Between these two extremes is a network of connecting branches that progressively consolidate individual cases into a single trunk. These connecting branches define the clusters. A level of consolidation that identified a set of seven clusters with similar characteristics, clusters A through G, was chosen. To accomplish this level of consolidation, a level of branching four steps from the individual cases on the one side and three steps from the trunk on the other side was chosen.

One can deduce from this discussion that cluster analysis relies to some degree on the subjective judgment of its user. I am satisfied that the consolidation level chosen produced a set of appropriately similar clusters that were not so numerous as to be useless nor so few as to lose important discriminations. Unfortunately, there is no automatic or standard way to choose a level of consolidation, but the content differences of the clusters created by my choices were striking and demonstrated internal consistency.

Appendix B: Data Collection Protocol

1. Case number

1a. Case code

Demographic Data

2. Age at last birthday

(1) <16	(7) 40–44
(2) 16–18	(8) 45–49
(3) 19–24	(9) 50–54
(4) 25–29	(10) 55–59
(5) 30–34	(11) 60–64
(6) 35–39	(12) 65+

2a. Age in years

3. Sex
   (1) male (2) female

4. Marital status at time of crime

(1) married	(4) widowed
(2) separated	(5) never married
(3) divorced	

5. Self-defined racial group

(1) white	(4) Chinese American
(2) black	(5) American Indian
(3) Japanese American	(6) other

5a. Self-identified as Hispanic?
   (1) yes (2) no

6. Highest grade completed in school

6a. If married, separated, divorced, or widowed, highest grade completed in school by spouse (or former spouse) (Code 99 if not married)

7. GED certificate?
(1) yes (2) no

8. Formal vocational skill training?
(1) yes (2) no

9. Nature of occupation (what individual does at work or instead of a job, even if not working at present; (e.g., student, housewife, mechanic, bank manager); be specific

9a. If married, separated, divorced, or widowed, occupation of spouse (or former spouse). (See Hollingshead's Four Factor Index of Social Status for codes; code 99 if not married)[a]

10. Employment status at time of arrest
(1) full-time
(2) part-time
(3) not working
(4) retired
(5) student

10a. If married, separated, or divorced, spouse's present employment status
(0) no spouse
(1) full-time
(2) part-time
(3) not working
(4) retired
(5) student

10b. Primary source of support during past year
(1) income from job
(2) income from government benefit
(3) income from retirement
(4) savings
(5) loans
(6) criminal activity
(7) alimony
(8) other

[a] A. Hollingshead, *Four Factor Index of Social Status*, unpublished communication from the author, 1975.

11. If unemployed, status at time of arrest
    (0) not unemployed
    (1) unemployed and not looking for work
    (2) unemployed and receiving welfare (AFDC, SSI, etc.)
    (3) unemployed, receiving unemployment compensation, and looking for work
    (4) unemployed, not receiving unemployment, and looking for work
    (5) full-time student

12. Past difficulty appropriately carrying out employment tasks?
    (1) yes (2) no

13. Past conflicts with employers (with teachers if student)?
    (1) yes (2) no

14. How many months unemployed (but not full-time student or homemaker)?

15. Family's gross annual income from all sources to nearest $1,000 (include welfare, unemployment, and investments)
    (1) $0–$4,999 (4) $15,000–$24,999
    (2) $5,000–$9,999 (5) $25,000+
    (3) $10,000–$14,999

16. Personal gross income from all sources to nearest $1,000 (include welfare, unemployment, and investments)
    (1) $0–$4,999 (4) $15,000–$24,999
    (2) $5,000–$9,999 (5) $25,000+
    (3) $10,000–$14,999

Psychiatric Data[a]

A. History of Psychiatric Treatment

17. Any treatment

[a] *Responses, questions 17–25K:* (1) at time of offense; (2) month prior to arrest; (3) past year; (4) ever; (5) never

18. Outpatient treatment

19. Inpatient treatment

20. Number of psychiatric hospitalizations

B. History of Psychiatric Symptoms

General Symptoms

21. Any psychiatric symptoms

Neurotic Symptoms

22a. Anxiety states—chronic

22b. Anxiety states—episodic

22c. Phobic symptoms

22d. Obsessive-compulsive symptoms

22e. Dissociative symptoms

22f. Conversion symptoms

22g. Extreme preoccupation with health

22h. Hypochondriasis

Depressive Symptoms

22i. Anhedonia

22j. Psychomotor retardation

22k. Cessation of normal activities

22l. Frequent crying spells

22m. Insomnia

22n. Significant despondency

22o. Hypersomnia

22p. Appetite disturbance

22q. Poor self-hygiene

22r. Diminished sense of self-worth or self-esteem

22s. Suicidal thoughts

22t. Suicide attempts

22u. Significant guilt feelings

Psychotic Symptoms

23a. Agitated behavior

23b. Manic behavior

23c. Bizarre behavior

23d. Episodes of depersonalization

23e. Episodes of derealization

23f. Hallucinations—visual

23g. Hallucinations—auditory

23h. Hallucinations—other

23i. Delusions—persecutory

23j. Delusions—grandiose

23k. Delusions—somatic

23l. Delusions—other

Abnormal Relationships

23m. Feelings of alienation or disenfranchisement

23n. Mild to moderate social isolation

23o. Marked social isolation

23p. Trouble relating to coworkers

23q. Trouble relating to schoolmates

Thinking Problems

24a. Impairment of consciousness

24b. Disorientation

24c. Impairment of memory

24d. Confusion/intoxication/delirium

24e. Difficulty concentrating

Behavioral Symptoms

25a. Pathological gambling

25b. Kleptomania

25c. Pyromania

25d. Preoccupation with aggressive thoughts

25e. History of explosive outbursts—chronic

25f. History of explosive outbursts—intermittent

Sexual Symptoms

25g. Sexual dysfunction (pain, frigidity, impotence, etc.)

25h. Egodystonic homosexuality

25i. Sexual identity confusion

25j. Sexual aberrations (fetishes, pedophilia, exhibitionism, etc.)

25k. Loss of interest in sex

C. Mental State at Time of Postcrime Assessment[b]

26. Any abnormal mental signs?

27. Status of mood
(1) normal (2) abnormal

27a. Depressed mood

27b. Anxious

27c. Manic

28. Physical appearance at the time of interview
(1) clean and well-groomed (3) disheveled
(2) marginal

29. Affect at time of interview
(1) normal
(2) blunted and/or constricted and/or inappropriate and/or labile

[b] *Responses, 26, 27a–c, 30–36b:* (1) yes; (2) no

30. Thinking at time of interview

    30a. Speech pressured

    30b. Flight of ideas

    30c. Communications lucid/coherent

    30d. Communications goal directed

    30e. Communications tangential

    30f. Communications circumstantial

31. Defendant suicidal?

    31a. Thoughts

    31b. Plans

    31c. Means

    31d. Prior attempts

32. Defendant currently homicidal?

    32a. Thoughts

    32b. Plans

    32c. Means

33. Ideas of reference present?

34. Delusions present?

    34a. Persecutory delusions

34b. Grandiose delusions

34c. Somatic delusions

34d. Other delusions

35. Hallucinations present?

35a. Auditory hallucinations

35b. Visual hallucinations

35c. Other hallucinations

36. Sensorium abnormalities at time of interview?

36a. Intoxication

36b. Confusion

36c. Disorientation
(1) none noted
(2) time
(3) place
(4) person
(5) two or three spheres impaired

36d. Memory
(1) intact
(2) short-term impaired
(3) long-term impaired
(4) both impaired

36e. Intellectual capacity
(1) above average
(2) average
(3) dull-normal
(4) retarded

36f. Adequacy of fund of information
(1) adequate
(2) inadequate

36g. Ability to solve problems
(1) adequate
(2) inadequate

37. Status of motor activity
    (0) normal
    (1) agitation
    (2) retardation
    (3) catatonia

D. Drug and Alcohol Use History[c]

Types of Drug Used

38a. Cocaine

38b. Marijuana

38c. Opiates

38d. PCP

38e. Hallucinogens

38f. Amphetamines

38g. Barbiturates or other hypnotic sedatives or minor tranquilizers

38h. Alcohol

38i. Others

39. Intoxicated from alcohol at time of offense?
    (1) yes (2) no

40. Intoxicated from drugs at time of offense?
    (1) yes (2) no

E. Primary Psychiatric Diagnoses

41. Axis I—psychiatric diagnosis (DSM-III)

[c] *Responses, questions 38a–i:* (1) use at time of offense; (2) abuse at time of offense; (3) dependence at time of offense; (4) use ever; (5) abuse ever; (6) dependence ever; (7) never used

42. Axis II—psychiatric disorder (DSM-III)

Crime Data

43. Type of crime (Record for each of first five victims; code 99 beyond actual number of victims)
    (1) homicide only
    (2) homicide/robbery
    (3) homicide/rape

44. Total number of victims

45. Relationship(s) to victim(s)
    (1) husband
    (2) wife
    (3) father
    (4) mother
    (5) son
    (6) daughter
    (7) brother
    (8) sister
    (9) other family member
    (10) boyfriend/girlfriend
    (11) friend
    (12) neighbor
    (13) acquaintance
    (14) stranger

46. Responsibility and intent
    (1) admits *neither* responsibility *nor* intent
    (2) admits responsibility *but not* intent
    (3) admits responsibility *and* intent

47. Primary motive
    (0) denies crime
    (1) crime as a by-product of a felony
    (2) romantic argument
    (3) argument over money or property
    (4) could not provide any rational motive
    (5) felt threatened
    (6) revenge
    (7) all others

48. Means
    (1) firearms
    (2) knife or other cutting instrument
    (3) blunt object
    (4) personal
    (5) other

49. Crime location
    (1) defendant's home
    (2) victim's home
    (3) other indoor location
    (4) auto
    (5) other outdoor location

50. Involvement of codefendant?
    (1) yes (no)

Impact from Environment or Situational Stresses at Time of Crime[d]

Stresses Related to Spousal Relationships

51a. Discord with spouse or significant other

51b. Separation from spouse or significant other

51c. Impending or recent divorce or dissolution of relationship

51d. Sexual difficulties in marriage or relationship

Stresses Related to Finances, Job, or Business

52a. Stress on job or in business

52b. Impending loss of job or business

52c. Loss of job or business

52d. Unhappy at work

52e. Impending or recent job change

52f. Financial difficulties

52g. Living in chronic poverty

[d] *Responses, questions 51a–58g:* (1) at time of offense; (2) prior to offense; (3) never

52h. Homeless

Stresses Related to School

53a. Dissatisfaction with school

53b. Doing poorly in school

53c. Impending or recent failure in school

53d. Impending or recent change in school situation

Stresses Related to Nonspousal Relationships

54a. Discord with friends and/or family

54b. Friendless

54c. Without family

54d. Without any social support system

Stresses Related to Health Problems and Death

55a. Serious personal health problem

55b. Loved one with serious health problem

55c. Terminally ill

55d. Loved one terminally ill

55e. Loved one recently died

55f. Recent loss of pregnancy (self or partner)

55g. Recent serious accident victim

55h. Loved one a recent serious accident victim

Stresses Related to Legal Problems

56a. Recently arrested (not in connection with current offense)

56b. Recently incarcerated (not in connection with current offense)

56c. Recently charged with a crime (not the current offense)

56d. Recently convicted of a crime (not the current offense)

56e. Involved in a civil suit

Stresses Related to Victimization

57a. Recent victim of property crime

57b. Recent victim of physical violence

57c. Recent victim of sexual violence

57d. Loved one a recent victim of crime

Stresses Related to Natural Phenomena or Developmental Milestones

58a. Impending or actual retirement

58b. Child's birth

58c. Child leaving home

58d. Move to new residence

58e. Victim of disaster

58f. Impending or recent marriage

58g. Impending or recent graduation or promotion

Childhood Data—General[e]

59. Suffered physical abuse as a child?

60. Suffered sexual abuse as a child?

61. Suffered significant neglect as a child?

62. Parents divorced during childhood?

63. Age at time of parents' divorce
(Code 99 if no divorce)

64. Institutionalized during childhood (correctional, foster care, or residential)?

65. Hospitalized during childhood (medical)?

66. Hospitalized during childhood (psychiatric)?

67. One parent absent for part or all childhood?

68. Both parents absent for part or all childhood?

69. One or both parents died during childhood?

70. One or more siblings died during childhood?

71. Father or paternal surrogate exhibited mental illness?

72. Father or paternal surrogate exhibited alcoholism or drug abuse?

73. Father or paternal surrogate exhibited criminal behavior?

74. Mother or maternal surrogate exhibited mental illness?

[e] *Responses, questions 59–82:* (0) no siblings; (1) yes; (2) no

75. Mother or maternal surrogate exhibited alcoholism or drug abuse?

76. Mother or maternal surrogate exhibited criminal behavior?

77. Relationship with father or paternal surrogate not satisfactory to good?

78. Relationship with mother or maternal surrogate not satisfactory to good?

79. Relationship with siblings not satisfactory to good?

80. One or more siblings exhibited mental illness?

81. One or more siblings exhibited alcoholism or drug abuse?

82. One or more siblings exhibited criminal behavior?

Childhood Data—Emotional and Behavioral Problems[f]

83. Trouble making friends?

84. Trouble keeping friends?

85. Friends tended to get into trouble?

86. Speech impediment unrelated to organic cause?

87. Unusual or extreme fears?

88. Sleep disturbance?

89. Eating disturbance?

[f] *Responses, questions 83–107:* (1) yes; (2) no

90. Bed-wetting beyond age six?

91. Encopresis beyond age four?

92. Fire setting?

93. Cruelty to animals?

94. Runaway behavior?

95. Frequent or chronic lying?

96. Frequent temper tantrums?

97. Frequent disobedience?

98. Stealing?

99. Vandalism?

100. Promiscuity?

101. Drug abuse?

102. Alcoholism?

Educational Data

103. Academic difficulties?

104. Behavioral difficulties?

105. Violent behavior toward students or teachers?

106. Truancy problems?

107. Attended special education classes?

Marital Data[g]

108. Number of marriages

109. Difficulty establishing or maintaining stable marital relationships?

110. History of spousal abuse?

111. History of marital infidelity?

Parenting Data[h]

112. Number of children

113. Contribution of at least some financial support to children

114. Maintenance of ongoing relationship with children

115. History of physical abuse of own children?
(0) no children (1) yes (2) no

116. History of sexual abuse of own children?
(0) no children (1) yes (2) no

117. History of significant neglect of own children?
(0) no children (1) yes (2) no

Criminal Data—Juvenile[i]

118. Homicide?

[g] *Responses, questions 108–111:* (0) never married; (1) yes; (2) no
[h] *Responses, questions 112–114:* (0) no children; (1) always; (2) sometimes; (3) not at all
[i] *Responses, questions 118–136:* (1) yes; (2) no

119. Rape?

120. Other sexual offenses?

121. Aggravated assault?

122. Armed robbery?

123. Other violent offenses?

124. Property offenses?

125. Drug- or alcohol-related offenses?

126. Spent time in juvenile correctional facility?

Criminal Data—Adult

127. Homicide?

128. Rape?

129. Other sexual offenses?

130. Aggravated assault?

131. Armed robbery?

132. Other violent offenses?

133. Property offenses?

134. Drug- or alcohol-related offenses?

135. Spent time in adult correctional facility?

Military Service Data

136. Spent time in military?

137. Type of discharge
    - (0) no military service
    - (1) general discharge
    - (2) honorable discharge
    - (3) dishonorable discharge

138. Court martial or time spent in brig or stockade?
    - (0) no military service
    - (1) yes
    - (2) no

Appendix C: The Composition of Proximate Causal Factors

Fourteen categories of proximate causal factors were identified for use in discerning distinct patterns of homicidal behavior and assigning murderers to clusters. Some categories represent composites; others reflect choices made from a discrete number of possibilities. The components of each category are specified below.

Only components documented as being present by objective evidence were included. Such evidence came from reliable informants; past medical or psychiatric records; court, educational, or social service agency records; or comparable sources. Corroboration by the study subject was taken into account but was not necessary for inclusion of a component. Components were not assessed as being present solely on the basis of information provided by the study subjects.

Each of the measures used was selected from a larger number of available possibilities on the basis of how well it reflected the causal factor being measured and how accurately and reliably the measure could be ascertained and corroborated. Some measures were excluded solely because reliability and corroboration were problematic.

The fourteen proximate causal factors and the individual measures associated with them follow:

1. *Interpersonal relations.* This factor is a composite measure. The capacity to establish and maintain satisfactory interpersonal relations was judged to be impaired if one

or more of the following indicators could be documented in the murderer's history:

a. Chronic discord with spouse
b. Infidelity to spouse
c. Pervasive neglect of children
d. Pervasive conflicts with others at work or at school
e. Chronic isolation and difficulty establishing any interpersonal relationships

2. *Impulse control.* This factor is a composite measure. Impulse control was judged to be impaired if one or more of the following indicators could be documented in the murderer's history:
   a. A pervasive pattern of impulsive outbursts
   b. A history of suicide attempts
   c. A history of aggressive outbursts
   d. A history of compulsive gambling
   e. A history of kleptomania
   f. A history of pyromania
3. *Reality testing.* This factor is a composite measure. Reality testing was judged to be impaired if one or more of the following indicators could be documented as being present at the time of the crime:
   a. Manic behavior
   b. Bizarre behavior
   c. Auditory hallucinations
   d. Visual hallucinations
   e. Other hallucinations
   f. Persecutory delusions
   g. Delusions of grandiosity
   h. All other delusions
4. *Rational thinking.* This factor is a composite measure. The capacity for rational thinking was judged to be impaired if one or more of the following indicators could be documented as being present at the time of the crime.
   a. Trouble concentrating
   b. Trouble thinking logically
   c. Bizarre thoughts
5. *Cognition.* This factor is a composite measure. Cognition

was judged to be impaired if one or more of the following indicators could be documented as being present at the time of the crime. Cognition impaired as a consequence of intoxication from substance abuse does not qualify:
a. Impaired consciousness
b. Disorientation
c. Memory impairment
d. Confusion

6. *Self-image.* This factor is a composite measure. Self-image was judged to be impaired if one or more of the following indicators could be documented in the murderer's history:
a. Pervasive feelings of worthlessness
b. Chronic guilt unconnected to an adequate cause

7. *Antisocial values.* This factor is a composite measure. Since antisocial persons will not necessarily acknowledge subscribing to antisocial beliefs, the status of antisocial values was measured indirectly by examining past patterns of behavior that would be indicative of such values. Four specific patterns were examined, and antisocial values were deemed present if one or more of the following four indicators could be documented in a murderer's history. Note that for adolescent murderers, juvenile criminal records were substituted for adult criminal records.
a. Adult non-violent criminality
b. Adult violent criminality
c. Spousal abuse
d. Physical abuse of children
e. Sexual abuse of children

8. *A Sense of alienation and/or disenfranchisement.* This factor is a composite measure. To be considered alienated or disenfranchised, one or more of the following indicators could be documented as being present at the time of the crime:
a. A lack of useful employment skills and/or involuntary unemployment six months in duration or longer
b. No discernible assets or resources and/or a family in-

come (personal income where appropriate) of $5,000 or less

c. Pervasive expressions of alienation from society; a sense of having been cheated or otherwise treated unfairly

9. *Axis I symptomatic psychiatric disorders.* This factor is not a composite measure. To be assigned to one of four diagnostic categories, a murderer must have met specific diagnostic criteria. The brief descriptions that follow provide an introduction to these criteria for readers who are not familiar with this subject. The precise criteria used in this study can be found in the third edition of the *Diagnostic and Statistical Manual of Mental Disorders* (DSM-III), which is published by the American Psychiatric Association and serves as the official diagnostic manual for all psychiatric diagnoses.

a. *Psychoses.* This category includes disorders in which impairment of reality testing is found. Symptoms may include incapacitating anxiety, disruptive perceptions in the form of hallucinations, markedly illogical thinking, bizarre content to thinking as is categorized by delusional beliefs, and severely disrupted affective states. Three subcategories of psychotic disorders are encompassed by the general category psychosis: schizophrenic disorders, paranoid disorders, and affective disorders.

Schizophrenic disorders are characterized by the presence of delusions or hallucinations, impairment or incoherence of thinking and communication, and impairment of affect (the emotional concomitant of communicated ideas). Schizophrenic disorders are discussed on pages 181–193 of the DSM-III.

Paranoid disorders are characterized by persistent persecutory delusions or delusional jealousy. An essential feature is the presence of permanent and unshakable delusional thinking. Paranoid disorders are discussed on pages 195–198 of the DSM-III.

Affective disorders are characterized by disturbances of mood involving either despondency or elation. There are several specific types of disorders, including bipolar disorder, major depression, and cyclothymic disorder. Affective disorders are discussed on pages 205–224 of the DSM-III.

b. *Psychoneuroses.* This group of disorders is characterized by the presence of psychiatric symptoms that vary in nature and severity but that in general are less severely incapacitating than psychotic disorders.

Included in this group are dysthymic disorders (depression), phobic disorders, anxiety disorders, and obsessive-compulsive disorders. *Dysthymic disorders* are characterized by despondency, a loss of interest in normal or pleasurable activities, and eating and sleeping disturbances. *Phobic disorders* are characterized by persistent and irrational fear of some specific object, activity, or situation that results in an avoidance behavior. *Anxiety* disorders are characterized by episodes of panic that occur unpredictably or by less intense anxiety that is chronic. *Obsessive-compulsive disorders* are characterized by repetitive thoughts or behaviors that cannot be resisted and are a source of discomfort to the sufferer.

Somatoform disorders also have been included in this category. These disorders are characterized by the presence of physical symptoms that suggest an organic disorder, but no organic findings and no explanatory physiological mechanisms for the symptoms can be found.

Dissociative disorders also have been included in this category. These disorders are characterized by sudden and temporary alterations in the normal state of consciousness. Involuntary motor behaviors may occur, important events may not be recalled, or an individual's identity may be temporarily forgotten.

Finally, *adjustment disorders* have been included in this category. The essential feature of these disorders is a maladaptation to some identifiable stressor.

The maladaptive reaction must occur within three months of the onset of the stressful irritant and be characterized by impairment in social, occupational, or educational functioning or by depressive symptoms or anxiety.

The disorders included in this category are described on pages 220–260 and 299–302 of the DSM-III.

c. *Substance abuse disorders.* This category includes disorders in which there is either episodic or continual use of substances that affect the central nervous system and result in behavioral changes. Substance abuse disorders are defined by a pattern of pathological use coupled with impairment of social or occupational functioning. The minimum length of the disturbance must be at least one month. In addition, these disorders require the presence of increasing tolerance to the effects of substances and/or a withdrawal phenomenon when the substances are withdrawn. Substance abuse disorders are discussed on pages 163–179 of the DSM-III.

d. *Behavior/organic/mental retardation disorders.* This category contains a diverse group of disorders that cause behavioral changes primarily socially maladaptive in nature. Four types of disorders are included in this category: psychosexual disorders, impulse control disorders, organic brain disorders, and developmental disabilities. The last two categories might have warranted a category of their own, but they were extremely rare in the study population.

The only *psychosexual disorder* associated with the study population was sexual sadism. This disorder is characterized by the intentional infliction of psychological or physical suffering to produce sexual excitement. In the study population, it was exclusively associated with homicide-rape cases. Psychosexual disorders are discussed on pages 261–283 of the DSM-III.

The *impulse control disorders* most often associated with the study population were intermittent explosive disorders and isolated explosive disorders. In these disorders, loss of control leads to aggressive behavior, which results in assault, homicide, or the destruction of property. In intermittent explosive disorders, outbursts occur periodically. Isolated explosive disorders are categorized by a single, discrete episode of aggressive behavior. Impulse control disorders are discussed on pages 291–298 of the DSM-III.

Organic brain disorders are characterized by cognitive impairment. They may involve a clouded state of consciousness, confusion, disorientation, and/or memory impairment. Perceptual disturbances may occur. When such syndromes are linked to specific causative agents (either toxins or disease processes), they are called organic mental disorders and the specific cause is cited as part of the diagnostic label. Organic brain disorders are discussed on pages 101–162 of the DSM-III.

Developmental disabilities or mental retardation comprise conditions whose essential features include subaverage general intellectual functioning, which results in maladaptation. The diagnosis can be made regardless of whether there is a coexisting mental or physical disorder. The onset of the condition must occur before age eighteen. Developmental disabilities or mental retardation can be categorized as mild, moderate, severe, or profound depending on the measured intelligence quotient. Developmental disabilities are discussed on pages 36–41 of the DSM-III.

10. *Axis II personality disorders.* This factor is not a composite measure. To be assigned to one of four diagnostic categories, a murderer must have met specific diagnostic criteria. The brief descriptions that follow provide an introduction to these criteria for readers who are not familiar with this subject. The precise criteria used in this study can be found in the DSM-III. Some of the personality disorders have been clustered together. Four categories of disorders were designated for the purposes of the study.

a. *Antisocial personality disorder.* The essential features of this disorder include continuous antisocial behavior that began during adolescence and persisted into adult life, an inability to sustain consistent work behavior, the lack of responsible adult functioning, and an inability to make or maintain intimate interpersonal relations. A more detailed description of this disorder can be found on pages 317–321 of the DSM-III.
b. *Borderline, paranoid, schizoid, and schizotypal personality disorders.* This category includes four personality disorders. They have been clustered together because of the type and degree of dysfunction that all display. Borderline personality disorders were far more common among the study subjects than the others.

   Borderline personality disorder is characterized by instability in interpersonal behavior, mood, and self-image. Interpersonal relations are frequently intense and/or unstable. Impulsive and unpredictable behavior is common. Marked shifts in mood often are noted in association with angry outbursts. A more detailed description of this disorder can be found on pages 321–323 of the DSM-III.

   Paranoid personality disorder is characterized by pervasive and unwarranted suspiciousness and distrust, which permeate all aspects of personality function. Individuals with this disorder ignore evidence that would dispel mistrust and suspiciousness. They are typically hypervigilant. A more detailed description of this disorder can be found on pages 307–309 in the DSM-III.

   Schizoid personality disorder is characterized by marked difficulty in forming social relationships. Persons with this disorder are observed to lack warmth and tenderness for others and tend to be indifferent to praise, criticism, and the feelings of others. They show little or no desire for social involvement. A more detailed description of this disorder can be found on pages 310–311 in the DSM-III.

Schizotypal personality disorder is characterized by thoughts, perceptions, speech, and behavior reminiscent of, but not severe enough to meet the criteria for, schizophrenia. These oddities may include magical thinking, bizarre fantasies or preoccupations, paranoid ideation, perceptual disturbances, and oddities of speech. Social isolation is common. A more detailed description of this disorder can be found on pages 312–313 in the DSM-III.

c. *Histrionic and narcissistic personality disorders.* These two disorders have been grouped together because both tend to be associated with highly dramatic or emotional behavior that is dysfunctional but is not usually as disturbed as the disorders described previously. Very few such disorders were diagnosed in the study population.

Histrionic personality disorder is characterized by highly dramatic behavior, which colors the nature of interpersonal relations. Individuals with this disorder frequently draw attention to themselves. They are prone to exaggeration, and minor stimuli can produce inordinate excitation. Such persons crave novelty and stimulation, quickly become bored with normal routines, and usually appear to be shallow. A more detailed description of this disorder can be found on pages 313–315 in the DSM-III.

Narcissistic personality disorder is characterized by an exaggerated sense of self-importance and/or uniqueness. Individuals with this disorder are preoccupied with fantasies of success, need constant attention and admiration, and feel a sense of entitlement. They tend to be exploitive in their interpersonal relations. A more detailed description of this disorder can be found on pages 315–317 in the DSM-III.

d. *Low-impact personality disorders.* This category includes five personality disorders. They have been clustered together because they are characterized by anxious, timid, or fearful behavior. Persons with these disorders tend to intrude less on the rights and sensibilities of others than do those with the disorders described previously. Instead, the disorders tend to impair a person's functioning to such a degree that he or she is less able to cope with life.

Avoidant personality disorder is characterized by hypersensitivity to potential rejection or humiliation such that there is an unwillingness to enter into relationships in the absence of very strong guarantees of uncritical acceptance. Individuals with this disorder are devastated by the slightest hint of disapproval. A more detailed description of this disorder can be found on pages 323–324 of the DSM-III.

Dependent personality disorder is characterized by a propensity to allow others to assume major responsibilities for important life decisions. Sufferers subordinate their needs to the needs of others, and they are unwilling to make even reasonable demands on others. A more detailed description of this disorder can be found on pages 324–326 of the DSM-III.

Compulsive personality disorder is characterized by a preoccupation with perfectionism. Individuals tend to be highly controlling and insistent that others do things their way. They focus on work and productivity to the exclusion of pleasure and have a preoccupation with rules, efficiency, and trivial details. A more detailed description of this disorder can be found on pages 326–328 of the DSM-III.

Passive-aggressive personality disorder is characterized by indirectly expressed resistance to typical demands for adequate performance at school, at work, or in social situations. Individuals usually resent demands for performance and express their resentment through procrastination, dawdling, stubbornness. or forgetfulness. A more detailed description of this disorder can be found on pages 328–329 of the DSM-III.

Developmental disorders begin during childhood and may persist thereafter. They are diagnosed when one or more specific areas of development, such as language, are retarded. Cases so diagnosed exclude those instances where development is simply slow and ultimately will reach normal status. Rather, this diagnosis is reserved for instances in which development is perceived to be retarded on a more permanent and pathological basis. Developmental disorders based on inadequate performance with respect to reading, arithmetic, expressive language, receptive language, and articulation can be diagnosed. A mixed form of developmental disorder involves more than one area of impairment. A more detailed description of specific developmental disorders can be found on pages 92–99 in the DSM-III.

11. *Substance Abuse*. Substance abuse could be diagnosed as the primary Axis I psychiatric disorder. It also was examined independently of any such diagnosis. Substance abuse is not a composite measure. It was considered to be a significant causal factor if alcohol or other substances of abuse could be documented as having been used on at least three occasions in the month prior to the crime. With respect to alcohol, such use had to be of greater magnitude than social drinking. The substances considered as having a potential for abuse included alcohol, opiates, hallucinogens, PCP, amphetamines, cocaine, barbiturates, modeling glue and other volatile substances, and marijuana. To substantiate the presence of substance abuse, documentation had to be available in medical, psychiatric, or substance abuse treatment records; physical evidence such as needle tracks had to be present; or reliable history from unbiased persons knowledgeable about the defendant had to be available. No information about substance abuse or intoxication was used unless it was validated independently of the defendant's statements.
12. *Rationalizing or justifying motives*. This factor is not a composite measure. A rationalizing motive was considered to be a significant causal factor if one of the following motives could be causally and temporally connected to the crime:

a. The homicide was committed in the course of a felony.
b. The homicide was linked to a romantic quarrel.
c. The homicide was linked to an argument over money or property.
d. The homicide was associated with circumstances in which the assailant felt threatened or at risk.
e. The homicide was linked to an act of revenge.
f. The homicide was linked to some other specific motive not specified above.

13. *Intoxication.* Intoxication is not a composite measure. Intoxication was considered to be a significant causal factor if evidence was available to establish that the assailant was intoxicated at the time of the crime. Both of the following criteria had to be met:
    a. Proof of recent use and evidence of the presence in the assailant's body of one or more substances that can produce intoxication, including PCP, modeling glue and other volatile substances, alcohol, marijuana, opiates, hallucinogens, cocaine, amphetamines, and barbiturates. Such proof could include a urine or blood analysis or observational information provided by reliable and unbiased informants. Observations had to document disturbances of perception, wakefulness, attention, thinking, judgment, impulse control, or control over speech or other motor functions not related to other causes.
    b. Evidence of cognitive dysfunction caused by the effects of alcohol or drugs, including clouding of consciousness; memory impairment; disorientation as to time, place, or person; or transient delusional or hallucinatory symptoms.
14. *Significant stress.* This factor is a composite measure. Stress was considered to be a significant causal factor if one or more of the following types of stress was affecting a murderer at the time of the crime. For a complete list of specific stresses considered within each type listed here, see variable categories 51 through 58 in the Data Collection Protocol (appendix B).

a. Stresses related to difficulties in spousal relationships
b. Stresses related to financial, job, or business difficulties
c. Stresses related to school difficulties
d. Stresses related to difficulties in nonspousal relationships
e. Stresses related to health problems, impending death, or illness of oneself or a loved one
f. Stresses related to legal problems
g. Stresses related to victimization
h. Stresses related to natural phenomena or developmental milestones

Appendix D: The Composition of Long-Term Causal Factors

Four categories of long-term causal factors were identified as having possible relevance to the etiology of homicidal behavior. Long-term causal factors refer only to conditions that were present in a study subject's childhood or adolescence and that could legitimately be thought to contribute to the genesis of violent behavior later in life. Within each category, three or more individual measures were listed. Each of the measures used was selected from a larger number of available possibilities on the basis of how well that measure reflected the category and how accurately and reliably the measure could be ascertained and corroborated. Some measures were excluded solely because reliability and corroboration were problematic.

For any study subject to be rated as positive for any category, one or more of the individual items must have been present in that subject's childhood or adolescent background. Only items that were documented by objective evidence were rated positive. Such evidence came from reliable informants; past medical or psychiatric records; court, educational, or social service agency records; or comparable sources. Corroboration by the study subject was taken into account but was not necessary to rate an item as positive. Items were not rated positive solely on the basis of information provided by study subjects.

The four long-term causal categories and the individual measures that have been included in each follow:

1. *Negative parental and/or sibling role models.* Modeling is an important aspect of the social learning process. Chil-

dren emulate important authority figures and peers in the course of growth and development. Both the value system and the behavioral model that a child internalizes and uses later in life are heavily dependent on the models to which the child was exposed earlier in life. Other influences also are important in the formulation of adult behavior, but these early models are crucial. Six individual measures that could be reliably assessed were included in this category.

a. Father or father surrogate engaged in criminal offenses prior to study subject's eighteenth birthday
b. Father or father surrogate abused or was dependent on alcohol or other substances prior to study subject's eighteenth birthday
c. Mother or mother surrogate engaged in criminal offenses prior to study subject's eighteenth birthday
d. Mother or mother surrogate abused or was dependent on alcohol or other substances prior to study subject's eighteenth birthday
e. An older, admired, or otherwise authoritative sibling or step-sibling engaged in criminal offenses prior to study subject's eighteenth birthday
f. An older, admired, or otherwise authoritative sibling or step-sibling abused or was dependent on alcohol or other substances prior to study subject's eighteenth birthday

2. *Instability in the childhood environment.* Calmness, predictability, and constancy are important attributes of the childhood environment. Their presence maximizes the likelihood that normal growth and development will occur. Children who worry about the stability of their immediate environment may become preoccupied, despondent, and/or resentful and may fail to develop a normal and adequate complement of baseline mental mechanisms or coping skills. Eight individual measures that could be assessed reliably were included in this category.

   a. One parent was absent for three or more months prior to study subject's eighteenth birthday

b. Both parents were absent for three or more months prior to study subject's eighteenth birthday
c. One or both parents died prior to study subject's eighteenth birthday
d. One or more siblings died prior to study subject's eighteenth birthday
e. Father or father surrogate was afflicted by mental illness sufficiently severe to cause disruption of the childhood environment
f. Mother or mother surrogate was afflicted by mental illness sufficiently severe to cause disruption of the childhood environment
g. A sibling or step-sibling was afflicted by mental illness sufficiently severe to cause disruption of the childhood environment
h. Parents were divorced prior to study subject's eighteenth birthday

3. *Lack of safety in the childhood environment.* A safe and secure childhood environment is crucial for normal growth and development. Abused or neglected children cannot develop normal baseline mental mechanisms, especially the ability to relate to others in an appropriately intimate way, because a sense of basic trust has not developed. Self-esteem also is likely to be damaged. Abuse may lead to the development of Axis I and/or Axis II psychopathology. Sexual abuse may lead to depression or sexually related pathology. Three individual measures were included in this category.
   a. Exposure to physical abuse during childhood or adolescence at the hands of any authoritative, older, and/or more powerful individual as manifested in threats and intimidation or physical harm. If a single instance, the incident must have been sufficiently severe to cause significant fear or actual physical harm. If repetitive, the cumulative impact must have produced a comparable result.
   b. Exposure to sexual abuse during childhood or adolescence at the hands of any authoritative, older, and/or

more powerful individual of either sex. Any abuse was considered to be significant.

c. Exposure to a pattern of continuing neglect that would cause the child or adolescent to lack the expected ingredients of a normal childhood environment, such as the provision of life necessities, emotional nurturing, and appropriate supervision and limit setting.

4. *Disruption in the childhood environment.* Normal growth and development can be disturbed when children are abruptly removed from what they perceive to be their preferred or expectable childhood environment. Such disruptions are especially traumatic when they occur as a consequence of other difficulties in a child's life and may initiate what subsequently becomes a lifelong process of alienation or disenfranchisement. Three individual measures were included in this category.
   a. Placement in a foster home, children's shelter, or juvenile justice facility regardless of duration prior to the study subject's eighteenth birthday
   b. Prolonged medical hospitalization of at least one month prior to the study subject's eighteenth birthday
   c. Psychiatric hospitalization regardless of duration prior to the study subject's eighteenth birthday

Appendix E: The Composition of Childhood Behavior Patterns

Five categories of childhood behavior difficulties were identified for use in examining the antecedent behavior patterns of murderers. This analysis was undertaken in the hope that it would provide a better understanding of the evolution of the ultimately violent behavior. Additionally, there was a hope that prediction ability might be enhanced by such an analysis.

Each category focuses on a specific area of childhood functioning that can become pathologically disturbed or maladaptive. Within each of the five categories, two or more individual measures are listed. Each of the measures used was selected from a larger number of available possibilities based upon how well that measure reflected the category and how accurately and reliably the measure could be ascertained and corroborated. Some measures were excluded solely because reliability and corroboration were problematic. For a study subject to be rated positive for any category, one or more of the individual measures must have been present in that subject's childhood or adolescence. Only items that could be documented to have been present by objective evidence were rated positive. Such evidence came from reliable informants; past medical or psychiatric records; court, educational, or social service agency records; or comparable sources. Corroboration by the study subject was taken into account but was not necessary to rate an item as positive. Items were not rated positive solely on the basis of information provided by study subjects.

The five categories and the individual measures that have been included in each follow:

1. *Evidence of psychiatric distress.* A large number of symptoms of psychiatric distress can occur during childhood and adolescence. Symptoms were chosen that were most likely to be recorded as abnormal and/or remembered by those responsible for the care and supervision of study subjects during that period of life. Other important symptoms of distress were not used because they were found to be less reliably remembered or documented. Six types of symptomatology were identified.
   a. Speech difficulties such as persistent stuttering or stammering for which no physiological or anatomical cause could be found
   b. Extreme and persistent fears that were not typical of normal childhood concerns or that lasted longer than would be expected
   c. Persistent sleep disturbances with or without repetitive nightmares
   d. Persistent abnormalities associated with undereating or compulsive overeating
   e. Enuresis, the repetitive lack of bladder control, after age six
   f. Encopresis, the repetitive lack of bowel control, after age four
2. *Evidence of disturbances of conduct.* A number of behaviors commonly are associated with conduct disturbances. Such behaviors often are associated with antisocial behavior, criminality, and certain personality disorders later in life. The behaviors included in this category, while maladaptive and antisocial, were not associated with formal criminal charges or sanctions. Five types of behavior were identified.
   a. Fire setting, as evidenced by one or more acts of deliberate fire setting or by a repetitive pattern of "accidental" fire setting
   b. Cruelty to animals, as evidenced by the deliberate torment of or infliction of injury on animals

c. Pervasive lying, as evidenced by a persistent pattern of dishonest statements to parents, siblings, teachers, peers, and/or friends
d. Pervasive stealing, as evidenced by two or more instances of stealing from the home or from some other private or public place
e. Vandalism, as evidenced by one or more instances of destruction or defacement of public or private property

3. *Childhood or adolescent criminality.* This category examines the pattern of childhood and/or adolescent criminality. Eight types of criminal behavior were identified.
   a. Homicide, including murder, manslaughter, and nonnegligent homicide
   b. Rape
   c. Sexual offenses other than rape, including sexual battery
   d. Aggravated assault and assault with intent to commit grave bodily harm
   e. Armed robbery
   f. Any other violent offense not enumerated previously
   g. Property crimes, including theft, burglary, and crimes involving damage to property
   h. Substance abuse offenses, including offenses related to possession of, intoxication from, and/or sale of illicit drugs
4. *School difficulties.* The difficulties included under this category related to school performance but not behavioral difficulties in connection with school. Two types of difficulties were identified.
   a. Academic problems that resulted in poor academic performance
   b. Repetitive truancy
5. *Problems related to interpersonal relations in childhood or adolescence.* The difficulties included in this category related to behavior at school, in peer group activities, and in relationships within the family. Nine types of difficulties were identified.
   a. Behavior problems at school that necessitated punitive or corrective action on the part of school authorities

b. Violent behavior at school directed at fellow students, faculty, or staff that resulted in suspension or expulsion
c. Difficulty maintaining a positive relationship with the father or surrogate father that was not the consequence of abuse or neglect on the adult's part
d. Difficulty maintaining a positive relationship with the mother or surrogate mother that was not the consequence of abuse or neglect on the adult's part
e. Difficulty maintaining a positive relationship with a sibling or step-sibling that was not the consequence of abuse or inappropriate behavior on the sibling's part
f. Trouble developing friendships, with few or no close friendships evident
g. Trouble maintaining friendships
h. A repetitive pattern of temper tantrums
i. A repetitive pattern of disobedience that necessitated punitive or corrective action at home

References

1. W. Willie, *Citizens Who Commit Murder: A Psychiatric Study* (St. Louis: Warren H. Green, 1975).
2. G.W. Barnard, H. Vera, M.I. Vera, and G. Newman, "Till Death Do Us Part: A Study of Spouse Murder," *Bulletin of the American Academy of Psychiatry and the Law* 10, no. 4 (1982):271–280.
3. J. Campion, J.M. Cravens, A. Rotholc, H.C. Weinstein, F. Covan, M. Alpert, "A Study of 15 Matricidal Men," *American Journal of Psychiatry* 142 (1985):312–317.
4. A. Daniel and P. Harris, "Female Homicide Offenders Referred for Pre-Trial Psychiatric Examination: A Descriptive Study," *Bulletin of the American Academy of Psychiatry and the Law* 10 (1982):261–269.
5. A. Husain, "A Study of Young-Age and Mid-Life Homicidal Women Admitted to a Psychiatric Hospital for Pre-Trial Evaluation," *Canadian Journal of Psychiatry* 28 (March 1983):109–112.
6. H. Petursson and G. Gudjansson, "Psychiatric Aspects of Homicide," *Acta Psychiatrica Scandinavia* 64 (1981):363–372.
7. J. Tupin, D. Mahar, and D. Smith, "Two Types of Violent Offenders with Psychosocial Descriptors," *Diseases of the Nervous System* 34 (October/November 1973):356–363.
8. M. Wong, "Abnormal Homicide in Hong Kong," *British Journal of Psychiatry* 123 (1973):295–298.
9. I. Sendi and P. Blomgren, "A Comparative Study of Predictive Criteria in the Predisposition of Homicidal Adolescents," *American Journal of Psychiatry* 132 (1975):423–427.
10. T. Harder, "The Psychopathology of Infanticide," *Acta Psychiatrica Scandinavia* 43 (1967):196–245.
11. P. d'Orban, "Women Who Kill Their Children," *British Journal of Psychiatry* 134 (1979):560–571.
12. P. Resnick, "Child Murder by Parents: A Psychiatric Review of Filicide," *American Journal of Psychiatry* 126 (1969):325–334.
13. J. Satten, K. Menninger, I. Rosen, and M. Mayman, "Murder without Apparent Motive: A Study in Personality Disorganization," *American Journal of Psychiatry* 117 (July 1960):48–53.

14. H. Gilles, "Homicide in the West of Scotland," *British Journal of Psychiatry* 128 (1976):105–127.
15. H. Gilles, "Murder in the West of Scotland," *British Journal of Psychiatry* 111 (1965):1087–1094.
16. P. Gottlieb, P. Kramp, and G. Gabrielsen, "The Practice of Forensic Psychiatry in Cases of Homicide in Copenhagen, 1959 to 1983," *Acta Psychiatrica Scandinavia* 76 (1987):514–522.
17. D. Pagan and S. Smith, "Homicide: A Medico-Legal Study of 30 Cases," *Bulletin of the American Academy of Psychiatry and the Law* 7 (1979):275–285.
18. R. Langevin, D. Paitich, B. Orchard, L. Handy, and A. Russon, "Diagnosis of Killers Seen for Psychiatric Assessment," *Acta Psychiatrica Scandinavia* 66 (1982):216–228.
19. J. Lanzkron, "Murder and Insanity: A Survey," *American Journal of Psychiatry* 119 (1963):754.
20. C.K. McKnight, J.W. Mohr, R.E. Quinsey, and J. Erochko, "Mental Illness and Homicide," *Canadian Psychiatric Association Journal* 11 (1966):91–98.
21. E. Tanay, *The Murderers* (New York: Bobbs-Merill, 1976).
22. J. MacDonald, *The Murderer and His Victim* (Springfield, Ill.: C.C. Thomas, 1961).
23. D. Abrahamsen, *The Murdering Mind* (New York: Harper & Row, 1960).
24. M. Guttmacher, *The Mind of the Murderer* (New York: Farrar, Straus, & Cudahy, 1960).
25. B. Cruvant and F. Waldrop, "The Murderer in the Mental Institution," in *Studies in Homicide*, edited by H. Wolfgang, 156–169. (New York: Harper & Row, 1967).
26. M. Guttmacher, "The Normal and the Sociopathic Murderer," in *Studies in Homicide*, edited by H. Wolfgang, 114–133. (New York: Harper & Row, 1967).
27. E. Tanay, "Psychiatric Study of Homicide," *American Journal of Psychiatry* 125 (March 1969):1252–1258.
28. W. Bromberg, *The Mold of Murder: A Psychiatric Study of Homicide* (New York: Grune & Stratton, 1961).
29. American Psychiatric Association, *Diagnostic and Statistical Manual of Mental Disorders*, 3 ed. (Washington, D.C.: American Psychiatric Association, 1980).
30. Daniel McNaughton's Case 10 C. & F. 200, 210–211, 8 Eng. Rep. 718, 722–723 (1843).
31. Durham v. United States, 214 F.2d 862, 874–875 (D.C. Cir. 1954).
32. California State Department of Justice, *Homicide in California, 1982* (Sacramento: California State Department of Justice, 1983).
33. California State Department of Justice, *Homicide in California, 1987* (Sacramento: California State Department of Justice, 1988).
34. American Psychiatric Association, *Diagnostic and Statistical Manual,* 129–159.

35. L. Wilkinson, *Systat: The System for Statistics,* (Evanston, Ill: Systat, Inc., 1988).
36. M. Aldenderfer and R. Blashfield, *Cluster Analysis* (Beverly Hills, Calif.: Sage Publications, 1984).
37. H. Romesburg, *Cluster Analysis for Researchers* (Belmont, Calif.: Lifetime Learning Publications, 1984).
38. M. Anderberg, *Cluster Analysis for Applications* (New York: Academic Press, 1973).

Index

About the Author

Richard Michael Yarvis, M.D., M.P.H., attended Columbia College. He later received medical and psychiatric training at the State University of New York, Downstate Medical Center, in New York City and training in public health at the University of Michigan. Dr. Yarvis has served as a forensic consultant to attorneys and courts for more than twenty years and has taught jointly sponsored law-psychiatry seminars at both the University of Michigan and the University of California, Davis. He also has served as the chief psychiatrist and director of substance abuse treatment programs for the U.S. Bureau of Prisons. Dr. Yarvis is currently the medical director of Canyon Manor Psychiatric Residential Treatment Center in Novato, California, and clinical associate professor in the Department of Psychiatry at the School of Medicine, University of California, Davis.